NHA Phlebotomy Exam 2022-2023

Study Guide with 400 Practice Questions and Answers for National Healthcareer Association Certified Phlebotomy Technician Examination

MONA LINDSEY

Contents

Chapter Three: **Routine Blood Collection** **31**

Chapter Four: **Special Collections** **56**

Introduction

"Trust yourself, you know more than you think you do."

- Benjamin Spock

While the notion of trusting yourself is freeing, it is harder to implement. When preparing for an exam in the health field, relying on intuition is near impossible. To become a phlebotomy technician, you must become familiar with specific information in biology, chemistry, and overall clinical skills. You must understand the material and logic and remember the facts to succeed.

Phlebotomy is an important clinical job promising as a career and on-field experience for aspiring doctors, nurses, physician's assistants, or other medical roles. Phlebotomy technicians draw blood and process it for health tests, donations, or research purposes. Such work deals with highly critical tasks that need training and practice, like inserting needles into veins, sterilizing tools, and handling samples with care. It also includes basic knowledge and understanding of vitals related to the circulation system, like pulse and blood pressure.

The phlebotomy technician is often the direct liaison between the patient and the laboratory. Because it includes regular patient contact, technicians must train in proper communication. They are responsible for explaining to patients the procedures and calming them down in preparation for taking blood samples.

To become a Certified Phlebotomy Technician, you must have a strong work ethic. That said, reaching this goal can be challenging and intimidating. While a phlebotomy training program sufficiently prepares you for the practical, hands-on side of the job, preparing for the exam is primarily up to you. Whether working or attending school while studying for the exam, you do not have time or money to waste.

This book offers a consolidated way to study for your NHA Phlebotomy Exam. Alongside comprehensive content about all the areas you need to know for the exam, you also have access to included practice exams. In this study guide, you will have a concise summary of all essential aspects of phlebotomy: safety and compliance, prepping patients, collecting routine blood samples, special collections, processing collected samples, and the core knowledge necessary for becoming a phlebotomy technician.

At the end of the study guide, you can check your progress with 350 practice questions inspired by previous NHA Phlebotomy exams.

Read this guide, take notes, and review any material you struggle with. Use the practice questions (and answers) to check if you are on the right track. As one of the leaders in full-length test prep manuals, Henley Test Prep aims to give you confidence in your knowledge and skill set. Preparing for your test is paramount to passing and becoming a full-fledged Phlebotomy Technician. Above all, trust yourself to overcome exam nerves and feel empowered by the concise resource at your disposal. Get started with your 2022-2023 NHA Phlebotomy exam preparation today.

Chapter One: **Safety and Compliance**

The topic of Safety and Compliance is an essential aspect of being a phlebotomist. Working with biological and chemical substances means there is a high risk for contamination of bloodborne diseases. At the very least, mishandling substances or lab equipment can lead to inaccurate blood results or harm yourself and your colleagues.

Workplace Safety Regulations

The primary workplace for the phlebotomist is in the laboratory, handling and processing blood samples and other specimens. Many risks abound in the laboratory, including the potential for biological, chemical, physical, radioactive, and musculoskeletal hazards. To avoid these dangers, the Occupational Safety and Health Administration (OSHA) provides rules and regulations nationally to ensure laboratory safety. Along with OSHA, there are also federal, state, and local safety regulations.

Follow these OSHA guidelines to prevent hazards and stay safe in the lab.

Personal protective equipment (PPE) are tools that offer a barrier between your body and harmful biological substances. The most common and crucial forms of PPE for phlebotomists are medical examination gloves and white lab coats.

Medical examination gloves are the phlebotomist's first line of defense. Gloves provide a sufficient barrier against contaminants in the substances you handle. Contaminants may also be present on lab work surfaces or other equipment. Wearing gloves at all times ensures you protect yourself and others from contacting potential diseases from such contaminants. However, wearing gloves most of the time *does not* mean reusing gloves. You must remove gloves properly when you finish handling a collected sample or substance from a patient before moving on to the next patient. A standard procedure is to remove gloves to avoid contact between the contaminated gloves and your skin.

Steps to remove gloves properly:

1. First, take hold of the cuff of one glove (Hand #1) with your forefinger and thumb of your other hand (Hand #2) without touching the skin of your wrist.
2. Second, carefully pull the glove off Hand #1 until it is half off and inside-out.

3. Then, use your forefinger and thumb of Hand #2 to fully peel off the glove of Hand #1. As you do this, simultaneously remove the rest of Hand #1's glove, creating a ball with the two gloves.
4. Throw the gloves away in a lined container.

Operational Standards Regulations

When handling blood samples, there are significant risks to watch out for:

1. Injuring patients during the blood draw
2. Failing to obtain the right specimens from patients
3. Inaccurate blood test results that are inconsistent from one lab or facility to another

When drawing blood, various tubes might have contaminants or additives. Thus, it is important to draw blood correctly to prevent contaminating the sample.

Order of blood draw:

1. Blood sample tube
2. Sodium citrate tube
3. Serum tube
4. Heparin tube
5. EDTA tube
6. Sodium fluoride/Potassium oxalate glycolytic inhibitor

HIPAA Regulations

All phlebotomists must be familiar with HIPAA regulations and how to apply them to their daily responsibilities. HIPAA stands for Health Insurance Portability & Accountability Act and was established in 1996 to protect patient information and give patients authority over their health documents. The 'Portability' aspect of HIPAA refers to the protection of health insurance for workers (and families) in the case of job loss. Under HIPAA, you must only use the minimum amount of patient information necessary for three reasons: Treatment, Payment, and Healthcare Operations (TPO). This includes any information or data that can be used to identify a patient, such as doctor's notes or billing information.

Ethical Standards

There is a general code of ethics applicable to all healthcare workers. The code of ethical conduct is what phlebotomists must remember in their scope of practice. As a phlebotomist, you must take accountability for your clinical tasks regardless of the tools you use. The following ethical guidelines are important to remember:

1. Duty to the Patient: Phlebotomists should focus on their well-being by considering how they communicate with the patient. There should be an effort to reduce patient injury or any disadvantage to their person.
2. Duty to Profession: Phlebotomists must show a degree of respect towards their profession, including their responsibilities, tools, and workplace. This duty means performing your tasks to the best of your ability, maintaining honesty and integrity, and nurturing positive workplace relationships with other healthcare workers.

3. Duty to Society: Meet all expectations posed by your workplace, institution, or community.

Lab Equipment Quality Control

The equipment you use is critical to the job of a phlebotomist. All institutions or facilities must maintain the quality of their lab equipment. As phlebotomists, you are also responsible for taking care of equipment, using it for its established purpose, and disinfecting it between uses to protect yourself and your patients.

Standard Precautions

According to the Center for Disease Control, standard precautions are necessary to protect healthcare workers, including phlebotomists, from being infected by a disease via blood samples or other substances. In 1996, the CDC Infection Control and Prevention Advisory Committee created guidelines for standard precautions all healthcare workers should apply. Standard precautions are an enhancement to the original universal precautions disclosed by the CDC in the 1980s that focused on preventing exposure to HIV, HBV, and other illnesses.

Standard precautions allow extra protection across situations that universal precautions do not cover. Standard precautions designate prevention methods for cases concerning bodily fluids such as vomit, feces, urine, sputum, and nasal secretions.

Transmission-Based Precautions

To avoid transmitting bloodborne pathogens, you must take precautions that prevent diseases from spreading via droplets, contact, or air. Transmission-based precaution (or TBP) aims to reduce opportunities for such pathogens to spread (OSHA) (Occupational Safety & Health Administration, n.d.).

Exposure Control

Every medical facility, laboratory, or institution must have an Exposure Control Plan that aligns with OSHA regulations. Phlebotomists must be aware of their workplace's plan and train in practices that control exposure to diseases.

In the case of exposure to a blood sample, remember the following methods. After physical contact with blood samples, you must wash the exposed skin and hands with soap and water. Facilities should have a sufficient supply of hand sanitizers around workstations.

Disposal of Biohazards and Sharps

Sharps must be disposed of properly after each use to avoid transmitting any bloodborne pathogens. Improperly handling sharps and other biohazards can lead to many risks. In facilities with low stock or shortage of sharps disposal containers, the alternative methods are recapping needles, recycling containers, or overfilling containers, which are hazardous to workers and patients, and lead to increased transmission rates.

The category of sharps includes needles, syringes, evacuated tube systems, and tube holders or winged butterflies. All phlebotomists are responsible for planning and handling sharps during the blood-drawing process. The World Health Organization (WHO) has clear guidelines for disposing of sharps. Your workplace should have sharps disposal containers near the sharps workstations. Sharps containers are usually red and labeled "Biohazard" and are resistant to leaks and punctures. Always ensure you dispose of sharps at your closest location rather than travel with the sharps to another disposal. When passing them along, place the sharps in a container first. Avoid passing sharps from one hand to another or another person. Do not manipulate, bend, break, or remove used needles. When throwing sharps in the container, close the container, keep it upright, and do not wait until it is full before replacing it. The standard is to replace the container when it is three-quarters full.

CLIA Waived Tests

CLIA stands for the Clinical Laboratory Improvement Amendments of 1988. This act designated that all lab facilities must be tested and cleared under FDA guidelines. Waived tests are test systems the FDA has allowed for use at home. Waived tests must be simple and as error-free as possible, but they cannot be completely accurate. Incorrect test results can result from tests performed incorrectly or instructions not followed to the letter. At worst, there may be a risk to one's health due to carrying out the waived test improperly. Waived tests are valid when considering medication changes, such as therapeutic drug testing that monitors the effects of prescribed medication on someone's body. Tests should be done by trained phlebotomists or other healthcare professionals in a lab to prevent dangerous risks of errors. Various laboratories can enroll in the CLIA program to become a CLIA waived test.

Aseptic and Infection Control

All phlebotomists must uphold regulatory standards in the case of blood contamination or infection spread. To practice effective aseptic and infection control, you must follow these preventative practices: Wear personal protective equipment at all times, maintain hand hygiene, and keep safe blood-sampling equipment at your disposal, as well as antiseptics.

Regarding blood-sampling equipment (a needle and syringe, evacuated tube systems, butterfly needle sets, etc.). The hypodermic needle and syringe must be single-use and should be immediately discarded together (all pieces included) in a sharps container.

To prevent infection, keep the following precautions in mind:

1. Do not manually recap the needle
2. Do not remove the needle in any way
3. Do not disassemble the hypodermic needle and syringe

Other equipment can reduce the risk of infection. Despite regulations, lab personnel may occasionally fall into discouraged practices like manually removing the needle and putting apart the needle and syringe. For example, safety features like needle covers, needleless transfer systems, and retractable lancets may be available if your laboratory invests in such items. Auto-disable syringes are not used in phlebotomy, despite their ability to avoid reuse.

Capillary punctures are when you draw blood from tiny capillary veins, and they require using a sterile device with safety features designed to retract the lancet automatically. This feature can protect you from sharp injuries and prevent reusing the needle.

To protect yourself, you must always wear non-sterile gloves during a session with every new patient. Gloves – latex or non-latex – must be well-fitting on your hands to avoid discomfort or any contamination if too loose. As a phlebotomist, you must remove gloves after seeing each patient to protect yourself and the next patient. Practice effective hand hygiene before and after wearing gloves. Other equipment like tourniquets should also be cleaned and disinfected, as the possible transmission of microbes may occur.

You should use other additional safety measures if more blood exposure than usual is a potential risk. In the case of arterial blood sampling, extra protection like masks and eye-protective visors may be necessary.

In summary, remember these tips to control infection transmission:

1. Use sterile (examination) gloves
2. Hand hygiene
3. Single-use blood-sampling devices
4. Discard needles in sharps containers
5. Disinfect tourniquets
6. Move or transport blood samples in labeled, washable containers

Taking care of your environment and post-blood sampling cleanup is also necessary. The following phlebotomy recommendations are essential for regular aseptic and infection control. Always clean the workplace, keep it uncluttered and continually wash their hands and surfaces (table, chair, wall, etc.) to avoid the risk of blood contamination. Before starting the blood-sampling procedure, ensure you wipe the venipuncture site with alcohol, disinfect thoroughly and avoid any contact with the skin. After the procedure, discard all used devices as soon as possible. A closed container is essential to prevent spilling the substance when transporting blood samples.

In the case of accidental exposure, follow the Post-exposure prophylaxis (PEP) policy. All healthcare facilities or laboratories include a PEP policy that you must familiarize yourself with, which usually includes rapid testing to assess infection. PEP takes into consideration potential exposure to HIV, HBV, and HCV. The sooner you implement PEP practices, the better, preferably within 7 hours after exposure. Antiretroviral therapy prophylaxis must be performed within 72 hours of exposure to correct the exposure's effects.

Hand Hygiene

Hands are one of the most significant transmitters of microbes and bacteria. According to WHO, several conditions make it easy for bacterial transmission by hand. First, pathogens may be on the patient's skin or clothes and travel to your hands upon contact. They may be available on various surfaces or in the hands of healthcare personnel. For successful transmission, the organisms must survive in the hands for more than a few minutes.

A major component that allows for easy transmission is infrequent or ineffective hand hygiene practices. Transmission occurs when healthcare staff goes to the next patient or is in contact with another object, a surface, door, wall, doorknob, etc., that the patient(s) may touch. (World Health Organization, 2009) If you work in a hospital, consider that all furniture in a patient's room, from the gown to bedding, may be contaminated with bacteria from shredded skin cells and can be spread by your hands. Moreover, improper hand hygiene can cause the transmission of pathogens via single-use tourniquet even before being used. One study revealed a 9% contamination rate of MRSA on tourniquets.

Many healthcare workers neglect proper hand hygiene practices for several reasons. The biggest reason is forgetfulness. The following common reason is that the frequent wearing of gloves may make healthcare workers feel it is unnecessary to wash their hands continually. Often, the workplace may be fast-paced, which means not enough time to properly cleanse hands after seeing patients.

Another factor with limited time is an understaffed facility where the workload far outweighs the healthcare worker's abilities. Depending on the facility, there might be a lack of sufficient hand hygiene supplies, at least not enough to keep every workplace station stocked. Some workers may simply understate the importance of hand hygiene due to a lack of awareness of the available research. Phlebotomists must be aware of several conditions to remain alert and deliberate in their work habits.

Unfortunately, gloves are not enough to prevent contamination, especially with specific stubborn viral pathogens. According to a study, there is a 17% chance of MRSA contamination via gloves. Another pathogen – vancomycin-resistant enterococci – can stick to gloves for an hour. Without proper hand hygiene, gloves are not enough to avoid exposure to illnesses. Over time, glove use habits may become lax, which leads to reusing gloves from patient to patient or continuing use despite any damage to the glove. Failing to change gloves between patients leads to the transmission of pathogens. Moreover, gloves do not protect completely against certain pathogens, like herpes or hepatitis B. Therefore, hand washing is not an extra step but an essential barrier to dangerous exposure.

Ground rules for gloves:

1. Gloves must remain in the original package until you need them. Do not take gloves and store them somewhere like your pocket or a bag until required.
2. Do not wash or reuse gloves.
3. If damaged or ripped, remove gloves and use a new one, especially if you catch it before a blood sampling session.
4. Always wash your hands after wearing gloves, regardless of glove damage.
5. If blood or other substances contaminates the glove, follow protocols used for exposure safety.

Hand hygiene includes handwashing and disinfecting hands with alcohol-based hand sanitizer. Washing remains essential to hand hygiene, and phlebotomists must hand wash regularly to protect themselves and their patients. You must use a sufficient amount of soap and lather it on every surface of your hands for at least 30 seconds before rinsing. As a rule of thumb, follow PPE removal with hand washing when hands are dirty or contaminated, in the case of potential exposure, or after using the bathroom, and before and after eating.

As for disinfecting your hands with hand sanitizer or alcohol-based hand rub, this option is available for when your hands are not visibly dirty. After removing gloves, use hand sanitizer before moving to the next patient and touching a potentially contaminated surface or object (anything around or in direct contact with the patient). Using hand sanitizer properly means pumping a generous amount into the palm and spreading it across the entirety of your hands until dry. Make sure your hands are completely dry before wearing new gloves.

Often, phlebotomists may experience skin irritation due to habitual hand hygiene practices and glove use. Skin irritation is a common reason for reduced compliance with good hand hygiene habits. Do not wash your hands and use hand sanitizer to avoid skin irritation. If you must, wait a while after hand washing to using the hand sanitizer. When washing hands, ensure water is cold or lukewarm, as hot water will dry your hands. Always dry your hands thoroughly with a paper towel to avoid spreading germs due to the wet environment. In the case of dry hands, do not bring personal hand lotions or moisturizers since some products might have ingredients – like petroleum – that reduce the effectiveness of gloves. Ideally, most healthcare facilities or laboratories may offer medical-issue hand lotions that will not damage gloves. If needed, use medical-issue hand lotion before donning your gloves, or aloe vera-lined gloves, if available. Another option is relying more on alcohol-based hand sanitizers over hand washing (unless hands are visibly soiled or contaminated).

Other things to remember with hand hygiene are your nails and jewelry. Nails create risks for hand hygiene and glove integrity. Nail beds are often an environment rife with bacteria. The standard regulation at healthcare workplaces is to keep nails short and clean. Long nails or artificial nail extensions can attract more bacteria and may cause gloves to tear. Jewelry, particularly rings, can also store bacteria for long periods and lead to potential transmission. Even hand sanitizer is not effective at decontaminating rings. Moreover, rings with studs or jewels may damage gloves. Avoid wearing rings and other jewelry that may come into contact with contaminants.

CPR and First Aid

Cardiopulmonary Resuscitation (CPR) is a critical protocol to resuscitate or re-start a heart that has ceased beating. All healthcare professionals, including phle-botomists, should be trained in performing CPR during emergencies, usually after cardiac arrest. CPR keeps a patient's blood pumping for as long as possible until the heart starts beating again or until extra medical help arrives for more effective treatment. The main advantage of CPR is that it increases the chance of survival after cardiac arrest. CPR can be performed manually or using an automated external defibrillator (AED), which is available in medical facilities. AEDs are more effective in defibrillating a patient.

Always call 9-1-1 for emergency medical help first before beginning CPR. To perform CPR, you can use either hands-only CPR or compressions accompa-nied by mouth-to-mouth breathing.

Hands-only CPR – or compression-only CPR – is when you only use your hands to do chest compressions at a depth of 2 inches into the chest cavity. Compressions should be aimed at the center of the chest and continue at a rate of 100-120 compressions per minute. Lock your arms straight, and all force should come from your upper body to achieve the minimum depth required. It is recommended to perform compressions-only CPR for emergencies outside the workplace, as using mouth-to-mouth on civilians can lead to legal issues.

For CPR consisting of compressions and mouth-to-mouth, you must alternate between the two at a steady pace and perform compressions for a count of 30, then provide two breaths mouth-to-mouth.

To do effective CPR, remember the following tips. Keep chest compression con-stant, with little interruptions. Do not lean on the patient between compression, and ensure your hands are in the right place, right in the middle of the chest (between the collarbones and the top of the ribcage). Making compression suf-ficiently deep is essential. Finally, do not hesitate to perform CPR depending on gender or patient identity. According to research, women are less likely to have a bystander perform effective CPR outside of healthcare environments, perhaps due to bystander discomfort and hesitation about overstepping physical bound-aries. Avoid gender-based biases in the name of saving a person's life.

Documentation and Reporting

One of the top reasons for laboratory service payment errors are improper or insufficient documentation. The most critical medical record errors are when there is a lack of a direct <u>intent to order,</u> which is a doctor's assertion to order a lab service for the patient, or when there is missing documentation to prove a medical need for the ordered lab service.

Several factors are required for correct medical documentation. First, before carrying out a lab service order, ensure that there is a need for a lab test to treat the patient's diagnostic information. Doctors must be clear on the purpose of the intent to order, and it should be a specific medical issue.

Furthermore, doctors must clarify exactly the type of lab service they are ordering. They must not do so casually, such as jotting down a note like "Blood test," which is not enough evidence for performing a lab service. An intent to order should match medical review requirements. A physician-signed order must plainly indicate the type of test needed. Alternatively, it can be an unsigned order with medical records that back up the need for the lab service. The medical record must be aligned with the service ordered for billing and insurance purposes. Suppose there is any confusion about whether there was a medical necessity for a lab service order. In that case, check the following records: doctor's intent to order, progress notes, lab results, and signature log (or attestation).

An <u>attestation</u> is a statement that the physician making the order must complete if they neglect to sign the intent to order. As a phlebotomist, be aware of standing orders and the lab services they signify. Moreover, as a healthcare professional, you must be dedicated to documenting the process of fulfilling the lab order and reporting lab results.

Today, most lab results and medical records are online, and you will have access to patient files and medical history. Each medical record will find diagnoses, prescriptions, and previous procedures or lab tests. This knowledge is essential for being cautious in reducing patient harm and staying safe from exposure to any viral illnesses. It is also for knowing the medical issue for which you are testing blood specimens. Medical records aim to connect various healthcare providers contributing to patient care for better communication of patient ailment and treatment. The phlebotomist may have to provide their reporting to add to medical records.

Other than medical records, you will primarily be responsible for lab results reporting, customarily done electronically. Phlebotomists will have access to a database of patient records to input their reports. You must remember the patients you collect blood for and any important notes you took during the session.

A few guidelines for phlebotomists documenting lab work: input all essential information like date and time, patient's actions or reactions, and any abnormal occurrences. For example, you must document if the patient was willing or refusing to complete the blood draw or collection of other bodily substances or if they refused to fast. Often, you and other phlebotomists and healthcare workers will sign off the document or database with initials. If you make any mistakes on paper documentation (which always requires wet ink), simply cross it off with a single line and sign your initials next to the change. As for electronic data entry, fix mistakes by following your workplace's specific correction policies.

Overall, a phlebotomist's reporting must be comprehensive and accurate. It is better to provide more information than necessary. To communicate medical terms, aim to use standardized medical abbreviations and always proofread or check to ensure your report is correct. Phlebotomists will undergo competency assessments that discuss their working knowledge and skill level in their profession and documentation of their hours for certification purposes.

Key Takeaways of Safety and Compliance

- Workplace safety regulations

  o According to OSHA guidelines:

    - Use PPE
    - Medical examination gloves
    - Operational standards regulations
    - Order of draw
    - HIPAA regulations

- Ethical standards

- Lab Equipment Quality Control
- Standard Precautions: CDC's standard precautions designate prevention methods for cases concerning bodily fluids such as vomit, feces, urine, sputum, and nasal secretions.
- Transmission-based Precautions: (or TBP) aim to reduce opportunities for such pathogens to spread.
- Exposure Control: In the case of exposure to a blood sample, remember the following practices – after physical contact with blood samples, you must wash the exposed skin and hands with soap and water. Facilities should have a sufficient supply of hand sanitizers around workstations.
- Disposal of Biohazards and Sharps:

  o Sharps must be disposed of properly after each use to avoid transmitting any bloodborne pathogens.
  o Improperly handling sharps and other biohazards can lead to many risks.
  o Sharps include needles, syringes, evacuated tube systems, and a tube holder or winged butterfly.

- CLIA Waived Tests: The Clinical Laboratory Improvement Amendments of 1988 designated that all lab facilities must be tested and cleared according to FDA guidelines. Waived tests are test systems the FDA has allowed for use at home.
- Aseptic and Infection Control

  o Do not manually recap the needle
  o Do not remove the needle in any way
  o Do not disassemble the hypodermic needle and syringe

- Tips to control infection transmission:

  o Tips to control infection transmission:
  o Use sterile (examination) gloves

    - Hand hygiene

- Single-use blood-sampling devices
- Discard needles in sharps containers
- Disinfect tourniquets
- Move or transport blood samples in labeled, washable containers

- Post-exposure prophylaxis (PEP) policy

  o All healthcare facilities or laboratories include a PEP policy that you must familiarize yourself with.
  o PEP considers potential exposure to HIV, HBV, and HCV.
  o Implement PEP practices preferably within 7 hours after exposure.
  o PEP policy includes rapid testing to assess for infection.
  o Antiretroviral therapy prophylaxis must be performed within 72 hours of exposure to correct the exposure's effects.

- Hand Hygiene

  o Use a sufficient amount of soap and lather it on every surface of your hands for at least 30 seconds before rinsing.
  o Follow PPE removal with hand washing.
  o Disinfect your hands with hand sanitizer or alcohol-based hand rub when your hands are not visibly dirty.

- Ground Rules for Gloves

  o Gloves must remain in the original package until you need them. Do not take gloves and store them somewhere like your pocket or a bag until required.
  o Do not wash or reuse gloves.
  o If damaged or ripped, remove gloves and use new ones, especially if you catch them before a blood sampling session.
  o Always wash your hands after using gloves, whether there was any glove damage.
  o If blood or other substances contaminates the glove, follow protocols for exposure safety.

- CPR & First Aid

- o Hands-only CPR or compression-only CPR is when you only use your hands to do chest compressions at a depth of 2 inches into the chest cavity.
- o Compressions should be aimed at the center of the chest and continue at a rate of 100-120 compression per minute. Arms must be locked straight, and all force should come from your upper body to achieve the minimum depth required.
- o Normal CPR consists of both compressions and mouth-to-mouth. Alternate between the two at a steady pace. Perform compressions for a count of 30, then provide two breaths mouth-to-mouth.
- o Keep chest compression constant, with little interruptions.
- o Do not lean on the patient between compression, and ensure your hands are in the right place, right in the middle of the chest, between the collarbones, and the top of the ribcage.
- o Make compression sufficiently deep.

- Intent to order: A doctor's assertion to order a lab service for the patient
- Attestation: A statement that the physician making the order must complete if they neglect to sign the intent to order.

Once you are confident in your knowledge of the Safety and Compliance section of the exam, it is time to move on to Patient Preparation.

Chapter Two: **Patient Preparation**

Being a phlebotomist takes much more than knowing the technical aspects of blood collection, maintaining health regulations, and managing lab orders. The role also necessitates clear communication and building rapport with the patients. As such, patient preparation is a fundamental aspect of phlebotomy, taking up its own section on the NHA Phlebotomy Exam. This chapter will cover the steps leading up to venipuncture, like explaining the process to the patient, addressing paperwork, preparing the patient, establishing lab testing requirements, and selecting the venipuncture site.

Identifying the Patient

Patient relations is vital for ensuring patients are relaxed during the venipuncture session. All phlebotomists must be professional and polite when speaking to patients and transparent about the process. When meeting the patient, you must introduce yourself and identify the patient for security reasons. Misidentifying your patient can lead to disastrous results. The best case scenario is that it could cause the medical bill to be sent to the wrong person. The worst-case scenario can lead to adverse effects, like increased hospital costs and transfusion deaths. Misidentification can cost hospitals up to $200-$400 million annually. ("Misidentified Patients and Samples," n.d.)

As such, phlebotomists must treat this issue with zero tolerance. Doing so can lead to a significant reduction in the risk of making identification errors.

Identifying the patient is a part of the introduction process. A proper self-introduction starts with a personal identification, in which you provide your name. For example: "Hello, I am [Name], and I am here to conduct your blood test today." Then, you will identify the patient for safety and rapport. Ask the patient's name and birth date and check if it matches the information printed on the lab order or requisition form. If inpatient or unconscious, check their ID bracelet for their identity, only if it is on the patient's arm. Do not consider an unworn ID bracelet as an acceptable form of identification. Do not proceed with blood collection if the patient does not have an ID bracelet. If the patient is alert but has limited communication ability for several reasons (i.e., speaking another language), a family member can also identify the patient for you. However, remember to note the family member's name in your report. Do not say them and ask if it's correct. You should ask, "What is your name?" For outpatients, you will fill out a requisition, an identification form on which you will write down their last name and birth date.

What happens if you do happen to misidentify the patient? Different facilities will have clear policies about this. In general, you must document all events of mislabeling. This documentation helps the facility improve its processes in case systemic issues lead to a high misidentification rate. It also allows you to understand how and why misidentification occurs as a phlebotomist. As for disciplinary action, this depends on your workplace and your unique situation. These factors will be analyzed first before deciding on your position as a phlebotomist.

Provide a briefing on your role and experience to reassure the patient. For example, you could say: "I am trained to do lab tests, and I have done it many times as a part of my role at this facility." Then, you may explain the current lab test's purpose and describe how the process goes. For example: "It looks like this lab test is to check for [purpose, according to lab order on patient's records]. Do not worry. It is a simple process. I will draw a tiny bit of blood with a small needle; then they will go to the lab for testing before being sent to your doctor, who will provide you lab results." Follow with an invitation for the patient to ask questions.

After introducing yourself, you may ask the patient a few standard questions to get them more comfortable before blood collection. For example, ask if they have any questions or need clarification. Ask them if they have ever done a lab test before, how they feel about the process, and if they have any fears about needles. It would be a good idea to inquire about their medical history of allergies or the potential to faint. Fasting before the lab test is required and seemingly obvious, but be sure to ask if the patient has indeed not taken any food before the lab test.

All patients are subject to protection under the Patient's Bill of Rights, provided by the Joint Commission on Accreditation of Healthcare Organization (JCAH). You must remember these rights when interacting with patients. The following is a summary of these rights:

- Patient has the right to ask for accommodations
- Patient has the right to access treatment regardless of race, sex, religion, national origin, or income source.
- Patient has the right to confidentiality and privacy of medical records. No one but a healthcare professional involved in the immediate treatment of the patient is allowed access to such records without patient permission.
- Patent has the right to know all details of diagnosis, treatment, and prognosis.
- Patient has the right to refuse treatment.

To explain the venipuncture procedure properly, here is a simple rundown:

Requisition Forms

A requisition is a form that must be filled out for each blood or specimen sample to be analyzed. The requisition forms are for outpatients and have a set of requirements you must meet. When filling them out, you need information like the patient's full name, sex, birth date, ID number, lab test ordered by the patient's doctor, the full name of the doctor, date and time of the lab test, and your initials as the phlebotomist. It may also require extra details about the type of blood collection, like the source, especially in cases where the doctor has ordered any specific testing about cytology, microbiology, or fluid analysis.

Consent

All healthcare professionals, including phlebotomists, must know what qualifies as patient consent. There are two types of consent: explicit consent and implied consent. Explicit or express consent is required for more extensive, riskier, or more invasive treatments, like a surgery, and is established in writing. Implied consent is for more routine treatments, like inserting an IV, or for anything that can assume the patient is willing to receive the treatment. For example, a patient shows implied consent by coming for their blood test after fasting for 24 hours.

Regardless of the type of consent, it must be informed. As a phlebotomist, you are responsible for giving patients the space to provide informed consent. Informed consent means comprehensively explaining the treatment, its purpose, steps, risks, and other information. You must ensure that patients fully comprehend the treatment, from taking their blood pressure to drawing blood.

For patients who are minors, you must receive consent from their parents or guardians.

If you cannot obtain a patient's consent but continue with treatment, this is called medical malpractice, and it can happen to any healthcare professional, including phlebotomists. Malpractice refers to a civil lawsuit patients have the right to take against any healthcare worker. Breaching consent can lead to severe lawsuits and affect your reputation in the field. Most medical malpractice cases are concerned with express or explicit consent since that is easier to prove. The patient must communicate – either written or spoken – that they accept the treatment in question. Remember that patients can take their consent back.

As a phlebotomist, if a patient sues you for medical malpractice, you might have to pay a fine fitting of the severity and extent of the malpractice. There is little chance of going to prison. Malpractice insurance is an option to protect your legal rights. Unfortunately, if you experience a lawsuit, your insurance premium may increase, leading to financial difficulty.

Patients are allowed to refuse care. As a phlebotomist, your patient may refuse a blood test or other treatments in your scope. Accepting their refusal does not mean you are contributing to the detriment of their health. Legally, any adverse consequences of refusing care are seen as a natural result of the health condition. That said, you should thoroughly provide complete information about what may happen if the patient refuses care and the risks involved.

Summary of information to disclose to the patient for informed consent:

1. Explanation of diagnosis
2. Prognosis if the condition is left untreated
3. Provide available treatments, with steps involved and possible advantages and disadvantages
4. Prognosis with recommended treatment
5. Any uncertainties with recommended treatment
6. Answers to patient questions

Venipuncture Equipment

- Needles: Needles in multiple bore sizes can be attached with a syringe, butterfly, single draw, or evacuated collection tube.
- Syringes: A syringe may be used with the butterfly needle or evacuated collection tube if you draw blood from a hand or a child.
- Alcohol Wipe: Wipes that have 70% isopropyl alcohol to disinfect the vein site before you insert the needle
- Evacuated Collection Tube: This is a tube that includes a vacuum to collect a set amount of blood. They have different additives; the color of the rubber stopper tells you what kind of additives they have.
- The Hub: A piece that holds the evacuated tube
- Tourniquet: This is an elastic band that ties around the patient's upper arm to make locating the vein easier
- Gauze Sponges: To be placed over puncture under adhesive tape after removing the needle
- Adhesive Tape: Cover up the puncture wound following blood collection to tape gauze sponge down
- Sharps Disposal Container: Units specially made to hold discarded/used needles. Must be near the work station to dispose of needles after blood collection.

- Iodine Swabs: Cotton swabs of iodine are involved in drawing blood cultures and testing blood alcohol levels.

Site Selection

In contrast to an artery, veins are thinner and less elastic. Arteries tend to pulsate beneath your touch.

Selecting the right place to insert the needle depends on the position of that vein in your arm. The most common vein to draw blood from is the cephalic and median cubital veins. Another vein site is the basilica vein on the inner arm and dorsal hand veins. Rarely do phlebotomists use foot veins for venipuncture, but it is an option if the other veins are unacceptable due to health reasons.

Never depend only on your sight to find the right vein. Always palpate first, using your second or ring finger to find the vein line. If you are struggling to see the patient's vein:

1. Palpate or massage from the patient's wrist up to the elbow
2. Lower the arm, so blood runs down and makes the vein more visible
3. Pat the vein site with a slightly damp, warm washcloth for 5 minutes before palpating the site again.

There are situations in which you must avoid venipuncture and select another site. Venipuncture can result in an inaccurate analysis if a patient has a hematoma (a severe bruise caused by blood gathering outside blood vessels). If the site has scar tissue or burns, it will be more challenging to do a venipuncture. Inpatients do not undergo venipuncture on the same arm as the IV or blood transfusion needle because this can dilute the blood specimen. If a patient has had a mastectomy (removal of a breast for breast cancer treatment), do not do venipuncture on the arm of that side since the lymphatic edema can skew lab analysis of the blood specimen.

Similarly, avoid limbs with edema in general. If the patient's arms have fistulas or cannulas, do not perform venipuncture on them until you have obtained a physician's permission.

In summary, do not do venipuncture….

- On an arm with a hematoma
- On a site that has scars or burns
- On the arm with an IV
- On the arm on the same side that the patient has had a mastectomy
- On a swollen limb

There are a few types of venipuncture phlebotomists may perform, including the general venipuncture, fingerstick, and heel stick.

How to Perform Venipuncture

Venipuncture DO:

- Mix tubes with anticoagulant additive eight times
- Allow venipuncture site to dry thoroughly from alcohol swab before inserting needle

Venipuncture DON'T:

- Use the smallest needle size for venipuncture
- Let patient tighten their fist for too long
- Leave the tourniquet on for too long
- Probe around with a needle if you miss the vein
- Pull syringe plunger back too rapidly

Phlebotomists must be aware of some common risks to avoid or essential things to keep in mind. Keeping the tourniquet on for too long can lead to several dangers. First, it impacts cell volume, which leads to hemoconcentration of some aspects in the blood that cannot be filtered from the sample, resulting in inaccurate test analysis. Hemoconcentration is an increased blood collection in the vein site, which can increase potassium or glucose in that area, thus affecting the blood sample. It results in water and other elements leaving the extracellular space, increasing aspartate aminotransferase (AST), which can falsely show signs of liver damage on the test results. Finally, leaving the tourniquet on for too long may also result in hemolysis, destruction of red blood cells, pseudohyperkalemia, and a falsely high potassium level.

The phlebotomist should know that certain factors can also impact the blood sample. These include stress, exercise, drugs, posture, and daily rhythms. Stress can cause the blood sample to have a high adrenal hormone value, more white blood cell count, and acid-base imbalance (especially in the case of rapid breathing due to anxiety). To avoid these as much as possible, aim to make the patient as calm and relaxed as possible and ensure they are ready and comfortable before venipuncture. As for exercise, a patient that has just done any physical activity may have higher platelet counts and an effect on their creatine kinase, aspartate aminotransferase, and lactate dehydrogenase. Posture can affect the lab test results, especially tests for proteins, enzymes, lipids, and calcium.

As for drugs, physicians may order samples for <u>therapeutic drug monitoring</u>. The blood draw must be done at a specific time and is dependent on the drug concentration in the body. Drugs have peaks and lows throughout the day based on the time taken and the dosage.

Requisition Forms Requirements

The requisition form must have the following information. (AlliedHealthTools, 2021)

- Ordered lab tests: Specimen, date and time to be collected, initials of the phlebotomists/staff who collected it.
- Barcode labels: Ensure that collected blood samples are identified correctly. Some forms must include more than one label for every test. Phlebotomists will remove these labels and place on specimen containers.
- Diagnosis/Purpose: Also known as the ICD-10/Dx Code, this part of the form uses a diagnosis code to track the medically necessary reason for the lab order.
- Patient information: Full name and date of birth, patient demographics, billing information attached, patient's signature.
- Ordering physician name and signature.

Patient Positioning

Patients can be sitting or supine. Note that there may be an effect on lab results depending on the patient's position. The following tests are significantly affected by positioning: albumin, globulin, enzymes, and hormones. Make sure the patient has about 20 minutes to rest before venipuncture, as standing right before venipuncture can shift blood concentration. ("Patient Position," n.d.)

Pediatric positioning ("Positioning Pediatric Patients," 2015):

- The parent will help with child positioning. If sitting on a lap, the parent must immobilize the child's legs between their legs, secure the child's torso with an arm, and anchor the elbow from which blood will be drawn.
- For a supine pediatric patient, the parent can gently restrain the child with an arm over the torso, the other arm holding the knees down, and a hand anchoring the arm for venipuncture.
- Remember that restraint is unnecessary if the child is calm and unmoving.

Variables Impacting Collection

The following common errors can affect collection ("Factors Affecting Blood Test Results," n.d.):

1. Alcohol not drying properly after disinfecting site.
   a. This can lead to hemolysis. Allow the alcohol to dry before inserting the needle.
2. Failing to follow the order of draw.
   a. Leads to contamination of tubes from other additives and thus inaccurate test results.
3. Underfilling or overfilling the tube.
   a. Affects the blood-to-additive ratio.
4. Leaving the tourniquet on for more than 1 minute.
   a. Leads to hemoconcentration. Remove when blood begins to flow through the needle and into the tube. Never leave on for longer than one minute.

5. Filling one type of tube from another type of tube.
   a. Incorrectly mixed additives skew test results.
6. Mixing two partially filled tubes.
   a. If the two different tubes have different additives, this can lead to inaccurate test results. If the tubes have the same additives, the ratio of blood to additive will be skewed, leading to inaccurate test results. If blood stops before the first tube is filled, start a new tube.
7. Using a half-filled tube for another blood draw attempt.
   a. Doing this stops the vacuum's power, not filling the tube enough. Also, it delays the inverting of the sample, leading to clotting. Avoid this situation by always using a new tube when performing another blood draw.
8. Collecting below or above the IV.
   a. The IF infusion may lead to inaccurate results. Ask a nurse to turn off the IV for 2-15 minutes before the blood draw. However, it is suitable to collect above the IV without turning it off, with permission from the nurse or physician.
9. Using a syringe and transferring it into a vacutainer incorrectly.
   a. Do not use a syringe to force blood into the vacutainer tube. Instead, use a blood transfer device and allow the vacuum to draw blood naturally.
10. Excessive probing with needles.
    a. Probing or repositioning needles too much can lead to hemolysis, contamination with interstitial fluid, and inaccurate test results.
11. A traumatic draw.
    a. A traumatic draw is too slow and may cause hemolysis.
12. Mishandling specific specimens.
    a. Failing to follow specific handling directions (i.e., instructions to chill or control light/heat factors) can lead to inaccurate test results.

Special Considerations

Consider the following factors that can affect lab tests. ("Factors That Can Affect The Laboratory Tests," 2018)

- Diet
- Exercise
- Posture

- Biological rhythms
- Age
- Pregnancy
- Medications

Testing Requirements

Fasting is a usual requirement for most blood tests, and it requires abstaining from food and drinks for 8-12 hours before a venipuncture. Nutrients can affect test results, making some diagnoses, like diabetes, challenging. The phlebotomist must ask the patient if they are fasting. If they are not, ask a physician for options to substitute for alternative tests. Otherwise, they will have to reschedule.

The following blood tests require 8-12 hours of fasting:

- Glucose tolerance test
- Blood glucose test
- Liver test
- Renal function test
- Vitamin B12 test
- Gamma Glutamyl Transferase (GGT)
- Lactose tolerance test.

The following blood tests require 12 hours of fasting:

- Thyroid function test
- Iron test
- Lipid profile

Non-Blood Specimen Collection

Remember the following about non-blood specimens: all body fluids may be infectious, so you must maintain standard precautions. Label all specimens with patient ID, type of specimen, and source. Apply the label to the container, not the lid.

Nonblood body fluid specimens include:

- Urine tests
- Feces/stool test
- Amniotic fluid
- Cerebrospinal fluid
- Gastric fluid
- Nasopharyngeal secretion
- Saliva
- Semen
- Sputum
- Sweat
- Buccal swabs
- Synovial fluid

Urine tests are the most common non-blood sample. The types of urine samples include random sample, first morning/8-hour sample, double-voided sample, times sample, and 24-hour sample, all of which use the clean-catch midstream method except for the 24-hour sample.

- Random sample - Can be collected at any time.
- First morning/8 hour sample - Collected in the first void (first urine sample right after waking up in the morning, when urine is most concentrated). Other 8-hour periods can be used to accommodate night shift workers or those with irregular schedules. For these patients, the bladder is emptied before lying down, and urine is collected after arising.
- Double-voided sample - This sample is collected after first emptying the bladder and then waiting until another specimen can be collected. This sample is a more accurate test for glucose testing.
- Timed sample - Collected at a particular time during 24 hours.
- 24-hour collection - The patient must discard the first-morning void before collecting the rest of the day's urine samples and must be refrigerated at 5 degrees Celsius.

Urine collection methods include:

- Regular voided - The patient must void as usual into a clean container.

- Midstream - The patient must start voiding into the toilet, stop halfway (midstream), then continue into a clean container.
- Midstream clean-catch - Used primarily for UTIs. The patient first cleans the genital area, then voids into the toilet, stops halfway (midstream), then continues into a clean container.
- Catheterized - The urine sample is collected via a catheter.
- Suprapubic aspiration - The urine is collected via an inserted needle in the bladder and drawn through.
- Pediatric - Young children who are not toilet trained can use a plastic bag in their diapers.

Specific urine tests:

- Urine creatinine clearance - Samples across 24 hours will be collected.
- Urine pregnancy test - The first-morning void is used to identify levels of HCG in the blood.
- Urine glucose and ketone test - Diagnoses diabetes or monitors glucose and/or ketones in the blood.

Minimum and Maximum Collection Amounts

The following are recommended amounts for blood drawing depending on the patient's age (The Harriet Lane Handbook, 1993).

- Premature infants: 90-105 mL/kg
- Newborns: 78-86 mL/kg
- More than one month: 74-82 mL/kg
- More than one year: 74-82 mL/kg
- Adult: 68-88 mL/kg

Key Takeaways of Patient Preparation

- Identify the Patient

  o Ask for full name

- o Get the patient comfortable
- o Use active listening
- o Respect the patient's bill of rights

- Requisition forms: A requisition is a form that must be filled out for each blood or specimen sample to be analyzed.
- There are two types of consent: explicit consent and implied consent.

  - o Explicit or express consent is required for more extensive, riskier, or more invasive treatments, like a surgery, and it is usually established in writing.
  - o Implied consent is for more routine treatments, like inserting an IV, or for anything for which it can easily be assumed that the patient is willing to receive the treatment.

- Patients are allowed to refuse care. As a phlebotomist, your patient may refuse a blood test or other treatments in your scope.
- Selecting the right place to insert the needle depends on the position of that vein in your arm. The most common vein to draw blood from is the cephalic and median cubital veins.
- Always palpate first, finding the line of the vein by using your second or ring finger lightly.
- Do not do venipuncture

  - o On an arm with a hematoma
  - o On a site that has scars or burns
  - o On the arm with an IV
  - o On the arm on the same side that the patient has had a mastectomy
  - o On a swollen limb

- Testing requirement: Fasting is a usual requirement for most blood tests, and it requires abstaining from food and drinks for 8-12 hours before venipuncture.
- Nonblood body fluid specimens include urine tests, feces/stool tests, amniotic fluid, cerebrospinal fluid, gastric fluid, nasopharyngeal secretion, saliva, semen, sputum, sweat, buccal swabs, and synovial fluid.

Chapter Three: **Routine Blood Collection**

This chapter gives a study guide for the Routine Blood Collection portion of the NHA Phlebotomy Exam. Phlebotomists must know the devices available for various procedures and contexts, how to select the right device, order of draw, palpating, and other techniques critical to routine blood collection.

Blood Collection Devices

- <u>Non-sterile gloves:</u> Phlebotomists must use latex gloves to protect the patient and themselves before every blood collection. Gloves reduce the risk of pathogen transmission. They must be snug and cannot be too loose or too tight.
- <u>Syringe:</u> A syringe collects blood from patients with smaller veins.
- <u>Butterfly needle:</u> This type of needle is used mainly for smaller veins or pediatric patients. They are needles with attached plastic wings that make holding and manipulating the needle much more manageable. To use, uncap the butterfly needle by the wings and insert the evacuated tube in the hub without puncturing the tube's rubber cap. Hold the needle in your dominant hand, bevel facing up, and insert the needle at a 15-30 degree angle.
- <u>Multi-sample blood collection needle:</u> This double needle is used to collect two samples. You insert one needle into the vein and allow the blood to be sucked into the holder through

- Tourniquet: A tourniquet is a band that you will tie around the arm of the patient, about 3-4 inches above the site selected for the blood draw. Tourniquets are vein compressors, so it restricts the flow of blood returning to the heart. The veins beneath the tourniquet grow and become more visible, making it easier to see the vein intended for a blood draw. The tourniquet must be removed immediately after blood is drawn before withdrawing the needle from the site.
- Antiseptic materials: Antiseptic tools are used to disinfect the venipuncture site in preparation for the blood draw, like alcohol pads. To use alcohol, open them using gloves immediately before the process. Use a circular motion to wipe the alcohol swab across the selected venipuncture site before immediately throwing the pads away in the trash.
- Safety trainer device: This device aims to prevent accidental needle pokes when facilitating blood movement from the syringe to the vacuum tubes.
- Blood culture bottle: This is the container you will use to collect the blood sample from a patient that may have a disease (i.e., bacteremia, septicemia).
- Evacuated Collection Tubes: These are plastic or glass tubes with different colored stoppers (rubber tops). The color aligns with the additive that is relevant to the diagnostic test. Fashioned like evacuated tubes, the vacuum pulls blood from the vein into the tube. Always keep extra tubes on hand just in case of malfunction. The tube is inserted into the butterfly needle hub without being punctured. This causes the tube to be pushed into the hub further and allows the top to be pierced. Thus, the blood is sucked in due to the tube's vacuum. Remove the tube right after removing the tourniquet. After the collection, turn the tube upside down and back about six to ten times so that the blood mixes properly with the additive. Never leave the tourniquet on for more than one minute, or it may result in hemoconcentration and incorrect blood test values.
- Microtainer tubes: These are smaller collection tubes made for finger or heel blood, which is used when using the arm is more difficult (usually for children or elderly patients).
- Labels: You must use labels to ensure the patient receives the correct testing at the lab. The label must include the patient's name, date of birth, and other information about the lab test or patient. Some labs generate and print labels electronically, while others prefer hand-written labels.
- Gauze/Bandages: After venipuncture, you must extract the needle and

place gauze over the site with gentle pressure to avoid spilled blood and allow the clotting process to begin. Secure the gauze with a bandage.

- <u>Sharps Containers:</u> Sharps containers are usually red containers used to safely dispose of all sharp objects, i.e., needles that have been used. For instance, you must dispose of needles, syringes, and lancets in sharps containers. These containers are labeled with a biohazard sign.
- <u>Blood drawing trays:</u> A blood drawing tray is a tray used to organize and provide accessibility to all the tools necessary for each procedure. The tray may be available at each work station, or it may be carried for mobile phlebotomists to travel to other locations easily.
- <u>Blood draw chairs:</u> These are the standard chairs used in medical facilities for positioning patients correctly. Most chairs feature a lever that adjusts the chair's height, an adjustable armrest, and a small attached table. Some may even include a reclining feature for patients who experience nausea or dizziness.
- <u>Centrifuge Machines:</u> A centrifuge is a device to prepare the blood sample for testing. Phlebotomists insert the tubes into the centrifuge, allowing it to spin for about five to ten minutes (depending on the tube and type of diagnostic test) at high speeds to separate the contents. You must put each tube at opposite ends to balance the machine, and there must be at least two tubes inside the centrifuge. If you are testing only one tube, place a water-filled tube (with the same amount of liquid as your testing tube) opposite the blood sample tube to be tested. Seal the centrifuge properly and ensure the temperature remains between 20-22 degrees Celsius.

Device Selection

Using the right device in the right context is essential for avoiding risky errors. There is a proper way to choose the correct tubes for different lab tests.

Use a winged butterfly needle with vacutainers to increase flexibility during challenging venipunctures. It is also for sessions where you must collect more than one tube.

Specimens to be tested are usually whole blood, serum, or plasma. Whole blood and plasma require anticoagulation. Use tubes with anticoagulant additives such as EDTA (ethylenediaminetetraacetic acid), heparin, and citrate (Pratisha, 2015).

- Lavender topped tubes have EDTA, which allows for plasma or whole blood isolation, and they are optimal for generic testing and hematology.
- Green topped tubes will have heparin and can be used to separate whole blood and plasma.

Serum is the optimal substance because it gives a cleaner analysis and fewer false positives. Use tubes that activate coagulation (cause blood to clot), like thrombin or silica.

- Light blue topped tubs have sodium citrate, activating coagulation for serum samples.
- Red, orange, and gold topped tubes are also for serum extraction via coagulation.

Other tests do not require separation of blood elements:

- Royal blue topped tubes are without additives and are utilized to analyze trace elements or analytes.
- Gray topped tubes are for testing glucose and lactate levels. These tubes contain potassium oxalate (an anticoagulant) and sodium fluoride (a preservative that reduces glucose consumption at room temperature). Gray tubes preserve samples for glucose testing for 24 hours.

Needle Gauge Sizes and Lengths

The recommended needle length should be 1 to 1.5 inches. While many needle gauges are available, there are three primary ones: 21, 22, and 23. The larger the number of the gauge, the narrower the needle.

- 16 Gauge: Only used in surgery or ICU. These needles are large and used for blood administration and rapid fluid transferring.
- 18 Gauge: Not for routine blood draws. These needs are relatively large and used for drawing a higher quantity of blood for blood donor units,

therapeutic phlebotomy, or for administering fluids rapidly for CT PE protocols. These needles come with an attached collection bag.

- 20 Gauge: These needles are mainly for patients with smaller veins.
- 21 Gauge: Used for routine blood draws and does not cause any significant discomfort.
- 22 Gauge: Used for temporary IV. These needles are too small to administer blood.
- 23 Gauge: Butterfly needles are used for narrower veins or if there are fewer sites to choose veins from. These needles can be used for children.
- 24 Gauge: The smallest needle and mainly used for pediatric patients.

Evacuated Tubes

The evacuated tube system is the most common method used in phlebotomy, much more than a needle and syringe because it facilitates the smooth transfer of blood from the vein into the tube. It prevents the risk of needlesticks, labeling errors, and collecting inappropriate specimens.

<u>Types of tubes (by color):</u>

- Royal Blue: citrate tube, 7.0 mL
- Red: No additive, 7.0 mL
- Light Blue: 3.2% Sodium Citrate, 4.5 mL
- Gold Top(SST (serum separator tube)): separating gel and clot activator, 6.0 mL
- Light Blue - Yellow label: Thrombin, 2.0 mL
- Green (heparin): Sodium heparin (100 USP Units): 5.0 mL
- Tan: K^2 EDTA, 5.0 mL
- Yellow: ACD solution A, trisodium citrate, citric acid, dextrose, 8.5 mL
- Pink: EDTA, 6.0 mL
- Pearl Top (Plasma Prep, PPT): separating gel and EDTA, 4.0 mL
- Lavender: EDTA, 3.0 mL
- Grey (sodium fluoride)

<u>Blood Amounts</u>

There will be different sizes of the color of tubes. To avoid fluid tissue contamination, draw 3-4cc of blood into the royal blue (sodium citrate) tubes before filling them. Each tube will correspond with a different type of test.

According to UC Davis Health guidelines, the minimum blood amounts taken for each lab test are:

- Amylase (Blood) → one small red or green tube → 2.5 - 2.8 cc blood
- Arterial blood sampling
- AIC
- ABG'ALT
- ALP
- AST
- BMP → one small red or green tube → 2.5 - 2.8 cc blood
- Calcium, Total (Blood) → one small red or green tube → 2.5 - 2.8 cc blood
- CMP → one small red or green tube → 2.5 - 2.8 cc blood
- GTT
- Liver Panel → one small red or green tube → 2.5 - 2.8 cc blood
- Magnesium (Blood) → one small red or green tube → 2.5 - 2.8 cc blood
- Osmolality (Blood) → one small red or green tube → 2.5 - 2.8 cc blood
- Phosphorus, Inorganic, Blood → one small red or green tube → 2.5 - 2.8 cc blood
- PT → Prothrombin time
- PTT → Partial thromboplastin time
- Culture and sensitivity (C&S)

Order of Draw, Tube Inversion, Angle of Insertion

Regardless of whether tubes are plastic or glass, syringe or tube holder, phlebotomists must follow the order of draw to avoid additives contaminating and affecting lab test results. The additive in each tube may carry over if the blood draw is performed in the wrong order. Additive carryover is usually due to a needle touching the specimen/additive combination as blood fills the tube. As a result, that tiny amount can make its way to the next specimen collected. Another factor that leads to additive carryover is tube inversion. This is when the tubes are filled in an inverted position, making it easier for the blood/additive to touch the needle, piercing the top.

Example of additive carryover:

- Clot activator carrying over to blue tube (for coagulation) leads to results showing a falsely shortened prothrombin time (PT)
- If EDTA in lavender tube carries over to tube testing for potassium (green, gold, red), it can lead to falsely increased potassium levels

Following the order of draw is critical to avoid life-threatening errors.

According to the Clinical and Laboratory Standards Insitute (CLSI) guidelines, begin with blood cultures, royal blue (no additives), red, light blue, SST (Gold), green, tan, yellow, pink, pearl, and lavender. If you are only using a light blue tube (coagulant-activating) or if it is the first tube, first draw and discard 5 mL of blood (UNC Medical Center, reviewed 2021).

A more specific order of draw is as follows:

1. Blood culture tubes (these are first so that the collection bottle tops are not contaminated by bacteria from the other tubes' undisinfected tops)
2. Sodium citrate tubes (blue cap)
3. Coagulation-activating additive (light blue top)
4. Serum tubes with or without clot activator, with or without gel separator (Red and gold cap)
5. Heparin tubes with or without gel (green cap)
6. EDTA tubes (lavender cap)
7. Glycolytic inhibitor tubes (gray cap)

Tube Inversion

To ensure the blood does not clot, the anticoagulation additive tubes should be inverted (or turned upside) and then right side up, about six to eight times (some recommend eight to ten). This helps the blood samples combine with the anticoagulant well enough to avoid clotting. The natural air bubble in every filled tube helps this process. Do not just tip the tube slightly; make sure you are fully inverting the tube. Slight mixing causes tiny clots to formulate, leading to inaccurate test results.

The Angle of Insertion

The needle should be inserted at a 15-30 degree angle.

Fill Levels/Ratio

There are specific fill requirements depending on the tube type. Some have specific amounts in mL, while others must be filled up to the line indicated by the bottle's label. In general, coagulation tubes should not be underfilled, or else they will give inaccurate results. Full tubes have a blood-to-anticoagulation ratio of 9:1. An underfilled tube will mean too much sodium citrate anticoagulant to the blood sample, which will provide a false prolonged coagulation time while overfilling will lead to wrong shorted coagulation time.

According to Gunderson Health System Laboratories, fill requirements in order of collection:

1. Blood Cultures - blue and purple → 10 mL for adults, 1-4 mL for children
2. 2.7 mL Blue-capped tube → To the fill line
3. 1.8 mL Blue tube (clear cap, blue cork) → To the fill line
4. 6 mL Red (PRT) → Enough blood for the test
5. 3.5 mL SST (gold) → Enough blood for the test
6. 3 mL Mint green (PST) → at least ½ full for CO2 only
7. 4 mL Lavender/Purple → at least half full (2 mL)
8. 2 mL Lavender → 1 mL
9. 6 mL Lavender (Blood Bank) → 3 mL
10. 4 mL Gray → 2 mL

Mix anticoagulants six to eight times, so the specimen does not clot. If using a syringe, transfer to tubes instantly and mix to avoid clotting.

To prevent contamination:

1. Flush line by drawing and discarding a minimum of 5cc of blood, except in the case of blood cultures.
2. Do not do a venipuncture above an IV site unless the line is clamped. Wait two minutes and draw 5 cc blood to discard.
3. Do not ever pour blood from one tube to another tube.
4. Blood culture collection always goes first.

Equipment Quality Control

All equipment comes with guidelines for maintaining quality. Blood collection tubes are labeled by specs and manufacturing information like tube volume, expiration, lot number, and additives ("Blood Tube Labeling Information," n.d.)

Tube Volume

The amount of blood a tube can hold is precise and must be followed. If a tube is over-filled or under-filled, it can affect test results. The blood-to-additive ratio is very critical to analysis accuracy.

Expiration Date

Always discards unused blood tubes if expired because expired tubes may become defective. The rubber stopper may break, and the vacuum may lose resistance and become poor at properly sealing the tube. Additives can also expire, especially certain anticoagulants, which may ruin specimens that must not clot (George, 2015).

Lot Number

The lot number on each tube provides information about what other tubes were manufactured alongside it. If there is an issue with many collection tubes, it is possible to check all those labeled with the same lot number and bring the issue to the manufacturer's attention.

<u>Additive</u>

Blood collection tubes tend to contain an additive that should be mixed with blood to prepare it for a specific test.

Tourniquet Application and Removal

Apply the tourniquet before palpating to find a vein. However, leaving a tourniquet for more than one minute leads to hemoconcentration. Hemoconcentration describes the phenomenon in which coagulation proteins accumulate quickly due to the constricted blood. On test results, it can show a false increase in lipids, proteins, ammonia, hemoglobin, calcium, or potassium. The pause in normal circulation increases platelet activation. All of these factors affect test results. Some factors that may be severely affected include fibrinogen, prothrombin times, and D-dimer.

Remove the tourniquet if it takes longer than one minute to find the vein. Wait two minutes, so blood circulation returns to normal, then put the tourniquet on and try again.

Palpation Techniques

There are four recommended veins to draw blood.

1. Median antecubital: The most preferred vein is located in the inner arm, anterior of the elbow joint. It is usually easiest to locate and is relatively painless.
2. Cephalic: The second most preferred vein is located on the lateral side of the arm.
3. Basilic: This vein is located on the medial side of the arm, but it poses risks as it is near an artery and nerve. There is also a higher risk of the vein rolling or collapsing.
4. Dorsal: Veins near the hand, wrist, or thumb. Select this vein only if all other veins are inaccessible.

Palpation of the vein is critical to finding it because it provides information about the vein's width, depth, and direction. Apply a tourniquet first before palpating to make veins more visible. Start loose, then tighten the tourniquet more as needed. To palpate, use your index and/or middle finger and press the vein firmly. Use enough pressure to depress the skin so you can check for a bounce back from the vein.

Despite palpation, some veins may be harder to access. This can be due to several reasons. Younger and elderly patients may have thinner veins, some patients may have more rollable, harder-to-find veins, and sometimes the patient may be dehydrated, making veins more collapsable or smaller. Avoid this by advising patients to hydrate well and avoid caffeine 24 hours before the test.

When palpating, do not tap the site to find the vein. This can lead to hemolysis which shows up as a falsely increased potassium level on test results.

Skin Integrity, Venous Sufficiency, and Contraindications

When performing a blood draw on anyone, you must protect the patient's skin integrity. This protection is vital for geriatric patients as their skin may be thinner and more delicate. After taking the needle out, keep direct pressure on the site using gauze for a more extended period as this helps prevent bruising. Use a soft bandage to avoid damaging the skin. Alternatively, you may wrap gauze around the entire arm and tape it down so that the tape does not come into contact with the skin.

Contraindications

There are very few contraindications. Usually, anyone can go through a blood draw. However, in some cases, it may not be recommended, or it may be more difficult. For instance, patients with severe anemia and blood disorders may need special considerations during venipuncture. Other contraindications for site selection include: not drawing blood from an infected site or near an infected wound. Do not draw blood from an area with trauma.

Antiseptic Agents and Application

Antiseptics are agents that prevent or destroy the contamination of microorganisms and bacteria. Antiseptics are necessary to disinfect the blood draw site before performing venipuncture sufficiently. The common antiseptic agents available to phlebotomists for use are

1. 70% isopropyl alcohol
2. 10% povidone-iodine
3. 70% ethyl alcohol
4. Tincture of iodine
5. Chlorhexidine gluconate (or chloraPrep)

When compared, there is no difference in how well each antiseptic style prevents contamination. However, alcohol swabs (70% isopropyl alcohol) are preferable due to their convenience and lower relative cost. Other non-alcoholic antiseptics are used if the patient is allergic to alcohol or in the case of a blood alcohol test.

Application

Before, the standard way of applying an antiseptic agent was to use a circular motion. The idea was that concentric rubbing would push bacteria back out from the site with each motion, but there was no evidence that this application mode was more effective than any other. Since 2017, the CLSI standards have edited their guidelines. The recommendation is to use friction when wiping the site with an antiseptic agent. Using a back-and-forth motion (with friction) is the most optimal way to cleanse a site.

After applying the antiseptic, let the skin dry for a minute. Any remaining antiseptic on the skin may affect lab results. Ensure the skin is completely dry to avoid pain and the risk of hemolysis during venipuncture. After completing the blood draw, use gauze rather than a cotton ball because the cotton fibers can prevent proper blood clotting when pulled away from the site.

Anchoring the Vein

Anchoring – also known as the anchoring system – keeps the patient's arm steady as you perform venipuncture. Anchoring keeps the veins in place, reducing the risk of a vein rolling or moving during insertion. It also enables you to switch out tubes without jostling the needle. In this system, there are two anchors you can and should apply.

Anchor 1: Place your non-dominant hand around the patient's forearm, holding it steady. Use your thumb to pull the skin around the selected venipuncture site taut. Keeping the skin tight allows the needle to pass through easily and painlessly. The other fingers should be grasping the back of the arm, right below the elbow.

Anchor 2: When inserting the needle, use your index finger and ring finger to steady your needle/device by acting as a buffer between the arm and the needle. In other words, hold the needle with your two first fingers below, stabilizing it against the patient's arm.

If drawing from the hand vein, you can anchor it by holding the patient's hand beneath their knuckles. The patient's fingers should be bent. The thumb should also pull the skin taut over the knuckles.

Once the arm/hand is anchored, insert the needle at a 15-30 degree angle. Smaller or shallower veins require a narrower angle. The needle should enter at a moderate speed. Too slow results in slight pain, while going too fast has a risk of either passing right through the vein or missing it. After inserting the needle, hold it still, so it does not move.

Problematic Patients: Signs and Symptoms

Fainting is a possibility when performing venipuncture. About 2.5% of patients may faint either during or after the procedure. This can be dangerous, as the patient may jostle the needle (if inserted) and can lead to the needle injuring the patient or touching a nerve, leading to permanent paralysis. Phlebotomists must know what to do to prevent any risk of injury for fainting patients and how to deal with a fainting patient.

First, prevent any issues by asking the patient about any history of complications during previous blood draws. Do not mention fainting or dizziness. Keep your question vague, as the likelihood of fainting can increase when brought to the forefront of the mind. For example, ask the patient, "Have you ever experienced difficulty in previous blood draws?" If the patient says they have a history of feeling dizzy, nauseous, or even fainting, then take preventative measures. Tell the patient to lie down during the procedure. If the venipuncture chair is adjustable, recline. As a preventive measure, never turn your back on the patient. Remain close by so you can catch them if they suddenly faint.

During venipuncture, watch out for the following signs of fainting: pale face, lightheadedness, dizziness, sweating, quick breathing, or hyperventilation. Check in with the patient if you see these signs. Pause if the patient tells you that they feel like vomiting and you have not inserted the needle yet. Help the patient regain steady breathing, provide a cold compress to cool the patient's forehead, and bring a basin or bag in case of vomiting. If the patient vomits, provide water so they can rinse their mouth.

If you have inserted the needle and the patient shows signs of fainting or has fainted, follow these steps:

1. Remove the tourniquet
2. Extract the needle
3. Activate the safety feature of the needle (to avoid accidental needle-stick injury)
4. Discard the needle
5. If you can, lay the patient's body down. Alternatively, if the chair is adjustable, recline it, or lower the patient's head below heart level to facilitate blood flow to the brain.
6. Loosen clothing if tight or restrictive.
7. Call for extra medical assistance.
8. The patient may benefit from water or juice once they regain consciousness.
9. Stay with the patient for at least 15 minutes after fainting, just in case.

10. Call the attending physician or nurse if the patient does not regain consciousness or respond.

Using ammonia inhalants is not recommended for bringing a patient back to consciousness as it can cause breathing problems in asthmatic or allergic patients.

Possible Complications of Blood Draw

Venipuncture come with some risks. Common risks include minor bleeding, nausea, lightheadedness, bruising at the puncture site, and possible infection. There are also more serious complications to be prepared to encounter, such as hematoma, arterial puncture, and excessive bleeding, to name a few.

Hematoma: This complication is when blood leaks into the tissues during or after a blood draw, which can look like a bruise and swelling around the puncture site. Usually, a hematoma can occur when a vein is too narrow or delicate. However, several critical errors by the phlebotomist during venipuncture can increase the risk of hematoma. Prevent hematoma by avoiding the following:

1. Blind probing or finding vein by sight and minimal palpation
2. Inserting the needle too rapidly, causing it to pass through the vein.
3. Inserting the needle too slowly, causing partial insertion into the vein.
4. Removing the needle before the tourniquet
5. Not applying enough pressure to the puncture wound after removing the needle.

In the case of a hematoma, remove the needle and put pressure on the site for at least two minutes. Follow with a cold compress for swelling.

Arterial puncture is caused by accidentally pricking an artery rather than a vein. You will know if this happens when the blood is scarlet red, fills the tube too rapidly, or pulses into the tube rather than smoothly and gradually flowing. If this occurs, <u>remove the needle immediately,</u> and <u>put firm pressure on the puncture site with gauze for at least five minutes or until you see the bleeding has ceased.</u>

Excessive bleeding: A patient may sometimes continue to bleed longer than usual. This excessive bleeding can be due to the patient taking certain medications like blood thinners or anticoagulants like aspirin. It helps to ask the patient beforehand and prepare. If a patient experiences excessive bleeding, apply pressure to the site for as long as it takes for the blood flow to stop. Ensure the patient keeps his arm elevated, with his hand above heart level. Call the patient's ordering physician if it takes longer than 5 minutes to staunch the blood flow.

Bruising: With every venipuncture, the most common complication is a slight risk of bruising.

Adjustments When Establishing Blood Draw

As the World Health Organization recommends, it is important to plan, perform the blood draw correctly, and maintain quality control. Phlebotomists must be ready to adjust and adapt to unexpected occurrences during venipuncture to meet these standards.

To avoid any serious complications, remember to avoid the following when choosing a venipuncture site.

1. Arm with hematoma
2. Areas with fluid retention or edema
3. Areas with scarring or burned tissue
4. Ares with fistulas or grafts
5. Arm with IV
6. From an IV cannula
7. Arm with PICC line
8. Arm with blood clot
9. Arm with blood transfusion
10. Arm on the side of surgery
11. Arm on the side of a mastectomy
12. Directly from or near an open wound or infection

The following areas are out of the phlebotomist's scope of practice:

1. Central venous catheter

2. Major blood vessels (i.e., jugular)

A nurse or physician may allow you to draw blood from an IV or PICC line in exceptional circumstances. Upon collecting samples, document the situation clearly, so that the lab analysis considers that the extra fluid infusions may influence results.

There are ways to reduce the chances of any complications or need for adjustments occurring during the blood drawing process. For example, ask the patient to focus on deep breaths during the process. Deep breathing not only gives them a task to distract from the blood draw but also reduces anxiety and the risk of nausea or fainting. It can also reduce any risk of movement, tense arm, or clenched fist that may affect the blood draw's success.

Always ensure you are behind and directly aligned with the direction of the needle. Do not be angled awkwardly, as it could affect needle insertion.

It is vital that what you are inserting the needle into is the vein. Palpating and feeling for the firm, spongy feel line is important for finding the vein. Do this by gently using your non-dominant index finger or middle finger.

In some cases, it can still be challenging to find. Place a warm washcloth on the site selected for several minutes to make the veins more evident. Heat and exercise dilate veins. Ask the patient to do light movements to get the blood flowing, like bicep curls.

When inserting the needle, you can adjust as you go along rather than remove the needle and try again. Start with a 30- to a 45-degree angle. As the needle goes in, slowly adjust its angle to the vein, bringing the needle closer to the arm. This way, the needle's bevel (or end) is right at the lumen (passageway) of the vein. Never probe or move the needle side-to-side (or laterally), as this can bring pain to the patient and widens the puncture. Moreover, it can increase the risk of running into a nerve or artery.

In the case of a rolling vein, you should maintain a firm anchor by keeping the arm steady and preventing the vein from being pushed aside by the needle. Remain vigilant of the patient's reaction to the insertion while waiting for blood flow. Once it starts, maintain anchoring as the tube fills with blood. Then, once filled, invert your tubes to prevent blood clotting, which could jeopardize lab analysis and spoil your efforts during the blood draw.

If you have tried once or twice and still can not get a successful blood sample, ask another experienced staff member to help you. Difficulty in blood draw is expected when the patient has a chronic condition that affects the blood volume. However, the CLSI does not allow more than three attempts to draw blood on a patient.

Label the sample immediately to avoid mislabeling issues that could pose potentially dangerous health risks to patients.

Needle Safety Devices

Needle safety features are included or attached to many needles. Such safety features allow the needles to be used and handled with one hand that can remain behind the needle.

Re-sheathing device: This feature is a shield that covers the needle and/or retracts the needle, i.e., needle cap and safety lock. An evacuated tube system needles come with pre-attached needle covers, which avoid reusing and keep the needle from cutting or puncturing anyone, decreasing the risk of spreading a pathogen.

Butterfly needle safety features: Butterfly needles do not lock over with a resheathing device. To activate the safety feature, press a button on the instrument following the blood draw. A spring mechanism will cause the needle to go back inside the device. Other butterfly needles may require manual pulling on the device to retract the needle.

Syringe needles: Syringes also have a re-sheathing device that covers the needle in a plastic cap and is attached to a tube holder. However, the syringe requires a transfer device to get the blood into a tube. Syringe transfer devices are used to safely and effectively accomplish this without needing to remove the tube cap and risk contamination.

Capillary Collection (and Order)

Capillary collection is any specimen drawn from a finger or heel (or earlobe). It is used for blood specimens from infants, neonates, or tests that only need a small amount of blood. Do not massage the site when preparing for capillary blood collection, as it can lead to hemolysis (false high potassium). To help find the capillary vein, use heat or a topical vasodilator to the site.

The order of draw for capillary collection to avoid any additives contaminating the next tube is as follows:

1. Lavender
2. Green
3. Gray
4. Red/yellow

The following tubes should be mixed a minimum of ten times to avoid clotting, which capillary blood samples can easily do: lavender, green, and gray tubes.

Bandaging Practices

Badaging and dressing the site post-procedure allows the puncture to heal properly and avoid infection. There is a 1 in 200,000 risk of infection. Medicated bandaids may not be necessary if the proper antiseptic process is taken before venipuncture. Consider non-medicated bandages since some patients may be allergic. For example, some bandaids contain nitrofurazone which can cause contact dermatitis in sensitive individuals (Dhawan et al., 2010).

Non-latex spot bandages are the most commonly used. Use gauze wrap with Coban for geriatric patients. Non-latex adhesive bandage or gauze and paper tape can be requested. Use a non-latex spot bandage if the patient is not on a blood thinner; otherwise, use a non-latex co-ban for patients with blotting tissues. For gauze, wrap it around the patient's arm before applying non-latex tape on top without touching the patient's skin.

Infants should get latex bandages for fingersticks and heel sticks.

Patients will tell you if they have allergies. If that happens, advise the patient to remove the bandage after 20 minutes if they have any issues.

Labeling Procedures and Considerations

Before being transferred to the lab, specimens must be comprehensively labeled. If containers are not labeled, the sample or specimen must be collected again. A label should include the following details:

1. Patient name
2. Patient medical record number
3. Patient location (in the facility)
4. Collection date/time
5. Specimen type/source
6. Test ordered/required
7. Ordering physician

If there is a missing or inaccurate label and the patient needs a lab test done immediately for emergency reasons, an Emergency Release Form must be filled out for uncross-matched Group O blood. The specimen container must include a specimen transmittal or clinic encounter form that matches the specimen label.

Post-Procedural Considerations

There may be side effects during and after the venipuncture. Although the risks are low, there are rare cases in which a patient may experience infections, vaso-vagal reactions, or nerve injury. Vasovagal reactions result in fainting (syncope) and hypotension (low blood pressure (Ohnishi, 2005). A nerve injury is the most critical complication, as it can cause permanent damage to limb function.

Consider complications during and following a procedure:

- Fainting: The patient may feel dizzy, decreased blood pressure, or lose consciousness. This is often due to vasovagal syncope. To treat, lie the patient down flat, raise their legs, and do not leave them alone. The patient also should avoid driving for half an hour.
- Hematoma: A hematoma may occur when:

  o The needle is inserted into a small vein
  o The needle passes right through the vein
  o The needle is only partly in the vein or extracted before taking out the tourniquet.
  o The phlebotomists searches for the vein blindly without palpating
  o A pressure bandage is applied to the area

- Hypersensitivity: Some patients are very sensitive to seeing their blood due to Type 1 hypersensitivity, which triggers a histamine response or an anaphylactic reaction.
- Infections: Immunocompromised patients may be susceptible to infections during and following the procedure. Let the patient know to seek medical attention due to pain, swelling, redness, and tenderness. Other patients may feel pain and tingling during venipuncture because the needle may have touched a nerve. Remove the needle immediately in this case, as it could lead to permanent damage. Other rare complications include phlebitis and sepsis.
- Skin puncture: This needle insertion is done for people with diabetes and pediatric patients, usually in the fingertips, heels, and earlobes.
- Petechiae: This is when capillaries burst, causing a smattering of small red or brown spots around the puncture area. Ensure the bleeding has stopped completely before the patient leaves
- Aspirin or anticoagulation therapy: If the patient is undergoing such therapy, do not leave the patient alone until excessive blood flow stops.
- Nerve probing: If the patient experiences a sharp, electric spark upon needle insertion, remove the needle immediately, as it may have touched a nerve.
- Arterial puncture: If an artery is accidentally punctured, remove the tourniquet, place pressure on site for five minutes until bleeding stops, and check pulse and blood pressure.

Phlebotomy can be performed on patients with too much iron or hemochromatosis or with too many red blood cells (polycythemia). Too much iron stored in the liver and other organs can damage organs. Regular phlebotomy allows such patients to reduce iron levels to an average level. For this procedure, 500 mL of blood is taken at each session. Let patients know they may be left with a small bruise for a few days following the venipuncture. Other symptoms they may experience include dizziness and fatigue. Recommend that they rest for 24 hours, eat well, and hydrate well (Healthwise, 2011).

After the procedure, phlebotomists must inform patients about what to do afterward.

Key Takeaways of Routine Blood Collection

Blood Collection Devices

- Non-sterile gloves
- Syringe
- Butterfly needle
- Multi-sample blood collection needle
- Tourniquet
- Antiseptic materials
- Safety trainer device

Device Selection

- For whole blood and plasma:

  o Lavender topped tubes (EDTA)
  o Green topped tubes (heparin)

- For serum:

  o Light blue topped tubs (sodium citrate)
  o Red, orange, and gold topped tubes

- Other testing that does not require separative of blood elements;

  o Royal blue topped tubes for trace elements or analytes.
  o Gray topped tubes for glucose and lactate levels.

Needle Gauge Sizes and Lengths

- The gauses 21, 22, and 23 are the most commonly used sizes.

  o 21 Gauge: Used for routine blood draws and venipuncture and causes no significant discomfort.
  o 22 Gauge: Used for temporary IVs and is too small to administer blood.
  o 23 Gauge: Butterfly needles are used for narrower veins or have fewer sites to choose the vein from; can be used on children.

Order of Draw

- Blood culture tubes
- Sodium citrate tubes (blue cap)
- Coagulation-activating additive (light blue top)
- Serum tubes with or without clot activator, with or without gel separator (red and gold cap)
- Heparin tubes with or without gel (green cap)
- EDTA tubes (lavender cap)
- Glycolytic inhibitor tubes (gray cap)

Tube Inversion

- To ensure the blood does not clot, the anticoagulation additive tubes should be inverted or turned upside and then right side up about six to eight times. This helps the blood samples combine with the anticoagulant well to avoid clotting.

The Angle of Insertion

- The needle should be inserted at a 15-30 degree angle.

Tourniquet

- o The tourniquet is applied before palpating to find a vein.
- o If it takes longer than one minute to find the vein, remove the tourniquet. Wait two minutes so that blood circulation returns to normal, then put the tourniquet on and try again to find the vein in less than 1-minute

Antiseptic Agents

- 70% isopropyl alcohol (Preferred)
- 10% povidone-iodine
- 70% ethyl alcohol
- Tincture of iodine
- Chlorhexidine gluconate (or chloraPrep)

Anchoring

- Anchoring is the process of keeping the patient's arm steady and veins in place, reducing the risk of a vein rolling or moving during venipuncture.

    - o Anchor 1: Place your non-dominant hand around the patient's forearm to hold it steady. Use your thumb to pull the skin around the selected venipuncture site taut. Holding the skin taut allows the needle to pass through easily and painlessly. The other fingers should be grasping the back of the arm, right below the elbow.
    - o Anchor 2: When inserting the needle, use your dominant hand's index finger and ring finger to steady your needle/device by acting as a buffer between the arm and the needle. In other words, hold the needle with your two first fingers below, stabilizing it against the patient's arm

Capillary Collection is any specimen drawn from a finger or heel (or earlobe). It is used for blood specimens from infants, neonates, or tests that only need a small amount of blood.

- Order of draw:

o Lavender
o Green
o Gray
o Red/yellow

Labeling: A label should include the following details:

- Patient name
- Patient medical record number
- patient location (in the facility)
- Collection date/time
- Specimen type/source
- Test ordered/required
- Ordering physician

After you have Routine Collections covered thoroughly, move onto Special Collections, which describes what to do in unique situations as a phlebotomist.

Chapter Four: **Special Collections**

Once you are comfortable with Routine Blood Collection, it is time to become an expert in Special Collections.

Peripheral Blood Smears

In cases in which a patient's blood cells must be examined, blood smears will be used. A blood smear is a blood test that analyzes information about red cells, white cells, and platelets. Mainly, it is used to know the shape and amount of such cells. Often, a doctor will order a blood smear if the patient is experiencing:

- Abnormal bruising
- Flu-like symptoms (chronic and unexplained)
- Sudden weight loss
- Unexplained infection
- Unexplained anemia
- Unexplained jaundice
- Rashes
- Bone pain
- Tracking a blood-related condition

(Krause, 2018)

Blood cells can reveal information necessary to diagnose blood disorders or other illness.

Red blood cells: These cells influence the movement of oxygen through the bloodstream. Any irregularities can be tracked to a vitamin deficiency or medical condition (i.e., sickle cell anemia).

Disorders related to red blood cells include sickle cell anemia, hemolytic uremic syndrome, iron-deficiency anemia, and polycythemia rubra vera.

White blood cells: As defenders of the immune system, white blood cells fight infection. Excessive or insufficient white blood cells could point to a blood disorder, inflammatory problems, or an inability to handle infections.

White blood cell disorders include HIV, Hepatitis C, leukemia (acute or chronic), lymphoma, parasitic infections, and fungal infections.

Platelets: Other irregularities could mean a patient has a platelet disorder (too many or too few platelets), which can affect blood clotting, thus leading to excessive bleeding.

Platelet-related disorders include thrombocytopenia and myeloproliferative disorders.

Other disorders that a blood smear can diagnose include liver disease, hypothyroidism, or kidney disease.

Medications affecting a blood smear's results include warfarin, over-the-counter medications, vitamins, supplements, NSAIDs, antibiotics, and glucocorticosteroids.

The blood smear process: Patients do not need any preparation before the blood smear unless other blood tests are ordered, in which case a fast may be required. The phlebotomist must sterilize the selected site of venipuncture, tie a tourniquet 3-4 inches above the site, select a vein, and insert a needle to draw blood. Then, the needle must be removed. Pressure will be applied to the site with gauze, after which a bandage will be applied. The entire procedure takes about five minutes.

The risks of a blood smear include bruising, infection, soreness, dizziness, and fainting.

Blood Culture Collections

A blood culture is a lab test that analyzes for any sign of infection via microorganisms in the blood.

Equipment

Here is a general list of equipment needed for blood culture collections:

- Butterfly/winged collection set
- Vacuette
- Aerobic bottles
- Anaerobic bottles
- Exam gloves
- 70% isopropyl alcohol swabs (or other antiseptic)
- 2% Chlorhexidine with 70% isopropyl alcohol applicator
- Gauze/cotton ball
- Bandage
- Labels (and pen to write identifying information)

Equipment for blood culture collections can be either a winged blood collection set or a syringe. Blood cultures bottles will usually have a fill-to-mark (or target fill level) marked on the bottle label. It tends to be about 10 mL. They should not be expired, damaged, or contaminated.

Bottle Preparation

When preparing the bottles, wash your hands with soap and water first. Then, remove the plastic cap off the blood culture bottles and clean the tops using an isopropyl alcohol swab, iodine swab, or chlorhexidine.

Skin Preparation

Always begins by confirming the patient's identity. Next, apply a tourniquet and palpate for a vein to select the venipuncture site. Prepare the selected venipuncture site with an alcohol swab or soap and water (if visibly soiled). Put on exam gloves, disinfect the site, and let it dry. Do not touch or palpate the site again before venipuncture to avoid contamination. Remove the tourniquet.

Attach the set to the collection adapter cap to use a winged blood collection. Insert the needle into the vein. The adapter cap should be placed over the bottle and pressed downwards. This will pierce through the septum. Keep the bottle below the venipuncture site's level, and allow blood to fill up to 10mL (for adults or 4m for children). Once filled to target and the aerobic bottle has been sealed, repeat for the anaerobic bottle. Label the collection bottles and ensure they are taken to the lab within two hours.

Cover the site with a gauze and bandage. Always follow the discarding process for all sharps used.

How many blood cultures you take, and the timing will depend on the suspected condition/the purpose for the collection. For instance, if a patient has an unexplained fever, two to three blood culture samples must be taken simultaneously via two separate venipunctures and two more sets of cultures 24-36 hours later. If a patient is suspected of having pneumonia or acute primary bacteria meningitis, two sets of cultures must be collected by separate venipunctures immediately. If there is a possibility of infective endocarditis, four blood culture sets must be taken during the first one to two hours of evaluation. If negative, it should be followed by four more 24 hours later (Henry Ford Health, 2022).

Volume Requirements

Blood volume is critical in accurately determining blood culture's contents. Blood culture volume directly correlates with blood culture yield. The higher the volume, the higher the yield. The standard recommendation is 8-10 mL of blood per session. (Henning et al., 2019) For every extra 1 mL of blood, sensitivity increases by 3%.

Order of Blood Culture Sites

1. Peripheral venipuncture
2. Hospital expert or IV team
3. Arterial puncture
4. Notify provider

Pediatric Volumes

Special consideration must be given to pediatric patients concerning blood collection volumes.

The following table is from the Children's and Women's Health Centre of British Columbia. It should be used to determine the right maximum volume during a blood draw. The maximum allowable volumes are based on the patient's body weight. In general, the maximum blood volume allowed per blood draw is 2.5% of the patient's body's total blood volume.

Body Weight (Kg)	Body Weight (lbs)	Maximum volume allowed in one blood draw (mL)	Maximum volume allowed in a 30-day period (mL)
3 kg	6.6 lbs	6 mL	12 mL
4 kg	8.8 lbs	8 mL	16 mL
5 kg	11 lbs	10 mL	20 mL
6 kg	13.2 lbs	12 mL	24 mL
7 kg	15.4 lbs	14 mL	28 mL
8 kg	17.6 lbs	16 mL	32 mL
9 kg	19.8 lbs	18 mL	36 mL

10 kg	22 lbs	20 mL	40 mL
11-15 kg	24-33 lbs	22-30 mL	44-60 mL
16-20 kg	35-44 lbs	32-40 mL	64-80 mL
21-25 kg	46-55 lbs	42-50 mL	64-100 mL

High risk pediatric patients include patients with chronic or acute illness with symptoms like low hemoglobin level, blood level depletion, or erythropoiesis due to the illness or due to treatment.

- Renal failure
- Bone marrow dysfunction
- Malaria
- Sepsis with disseminated intravascular coagulation
- Anemia
- Patients treated with chemotherapy

Throat Cultures, Nasal Swabs

A throat culture is a test phlebotomists do to analyze infection-causing bacteria in the throat, especially strep. The ordering physician will order throat cultures if strep throat is suspected. It can also help determine the right treatment antibiotic (MedlinePlus).

Before the throat culture, advise the patient to avoid using antiseptic mouthwash before the throat culture test.

To perform throat cultures, the phlebotomist must direct the patient to tilt his head back and open the mouth. Advise the patient to avoid gagging or closing their mouth during the procedure. Swipe a long sterile cotton swab across the back of the throat. For a rapid strep test, use two swabs.

Secretions from the nasopharynx and tonsillar areas identify a pathogenic organism.

Throat cultures are also used for molecular tests (PCR) to check for COVID-19. A PCR test uses nuclein acid-amplification technology to find information that determines if the patient is infected with COVID-19.

Nasopharyngeal (NP) Culture Swabs

This tests the nasal cavity and pharynx using a cotton-tipped swab with a bendable wire that can be inserted into the nose gently. When removing it from the nostril, rotate it. This test is primarily used for whooping cough.

Blood Alcohol Collection

A blood alcohol collection test is used to check the level of alcohol in a body. Typically, this test is used for drinking and driving situations.

When preparing for blood alcohol collection, do not use an alcohol swab or iodine (betadine) on the site before a blood alcohol test. Clean the site with a non-alcoholic disinfectant/antiseptic such as hydrogen peroxide or green surgical soap. There must be a chain of custody for legal purposes. A specific tube containing potassium oxalate is necessary for this particular collection.

A phlebotomist can only attempt a blood alcohol collection twice. If a phlebotomist cannot perform the venipuncture the second time, a more experienced phlebotomist must step in. (ExpressLab, n.d.)

Key Takeaways of Special Collections

Peripheral Blood Smears

- A blood smear is a blood test that analyzes information about red cells, white cells, and platelets.
- Red blood cells influence the movement of oxygen through the bloodstream. Any irregularities can be tracked to a vitamin deficiency or medical condition (i.e., sickle cell anemia).

o   Disorders related to red blood cells include sickle cell anemia, hemolytic uremic syndrome, iron-deficiency anemia, and polycythemia rubra vera.

- White blood cells: Fight infection. Excessive or insufficient white blood cells could point to a blood disorder, inflammatory problems, or an inability to handle infections.

    o   White blood cell disorders include HIV, hepatitis C, leukemia (acute or chronic), lymphoma, parasitic infections, and fungal infections.

- Platelets: Other irregularities could mean a patient has a platelet disorder (too many or too few platelets), which can affect blood clotting, thus leading to excessive bleeding.

    o   Platelet-related disorders include thrombocytopenia and myeloproliferative disorders.

Blood Culture Collections

- A blood culture is a lab test that analyzes for any sign of infection via microorganisms in the blood.
- It requires anaerobic and aerobic collection bottles.
- When preparing the bottles, wash your hands with soap and water first. Then, remove the plastic cap off the blood culture bottles and clean the tops using an isopropyl alcohol swab, iodine swab, or chlorhexidine.
- The standard recommendation for adults is 8-10 mL of blood per blood draw.
- Blood cultures always go first in the order of draw.

Pediatric Volumes

- For pediatric patients, the maximum blood volume allowed per blood draw is 2.5% of the patient's body's total blood volume.

Throat Cultures, Nasal Swabs

- A throat culture is a test phlebotomists do to analyze infection-causing bacteria in the throat (i.e., if strep throat is suspected) or figure out the right antibiotic for treatment.

Blood Alcohol Collection

- A blood alcohol collection test is used to check the level of alcohol in a body and is typically used for drinking and driving situations.
- Do not use an alcohol swab or iodine (betadine) on the site before a blood alcohol test.
- There must be a chain of custody for legal purposes.
- For this particular collection, a specific potassium oxalate tube is necessary.
- Only attempt blood alcohol collection twice. Ask for another staff member's assistance if the second attempt is unsuccessful.

In the next chapter, we will discuss the Processing aspect of a phlebotomist's job.

Chapter Five: **Processing**

This chapter gives a study guide for the Processing portion of the NHA Phlebotomy Exam.

Centrifuging

After blood collection, never open any tube. Keep all tubes stored in a vertical, upright position.

Centrifugation requires proper training by a lab or facility. To centrifuge, ensure that gloves and lab coats are worn. Make sure all tubes remain sealed with stoppers when placed into the centrifuge. When loading the centrifuge, there must be an equal number of tubes of equal size and the weight inside the rotor head and must be placed symmetrically. If there is an imbalance, it can lead to poor centrifugation, and the blood sample contents will not be adequately separated.

Once the centrifuge is loaded, close and lock it. Turn it on, which can be made evident by the indicator light. When complete, it will stop. The centrifuge must be powered and cleaned off after use.

If the centrifuge is emitting weird noises or vibrating unusually, turn it off by pressing the power brake and unplug the centrifuge. Check the source of the problem or call an experienced staff member for help.

Centrifuged tubes include red top tubes that should clot for about an hour at room temperature before centrifuging for ten minutes. Red topped tubes do not have a gel separator and are used for chemistry and serology (serum) testing.

Gold topped tubers have a clot-activating additive and a gel separator. All gold topped tubes should clot for 30 minutes before centrifuging for ten minutes. This clotting allows the gel to separate the serum from the blood, which is why it is called a gel barrier. Centrifuge gold tubes as soon as possible.

All tubes with gel barriers should be centrifuged before transportation to separate serum and plasma from the gel barrier cells.

Green tubes, which contain lithium heparin, are used for sodium level tests. Centrifuge these tubes for ten minutes.

BD blue tubes should be centrifuged for 15 minutes.

SST – or serum separator tubes – are meant for extracting serum. They contain clot activating additives and serum separator gel, which allow blood samples to clot in at least 30 minutes. The tube must sit upright at room temperature for 30-45 minutes, then centrifuged for ten minutes at 3400 rpm. To process an SST tube, collect blood, invert the tubes eight times, and centrifuge for 15 minutes at 2200-2500 rpm for no later than an hour after collecting the sample.

PST stands for Plasma Separate Tube, and the additives include lithium heparin and plasma separator gel. Both SST and PST tubes allow for separation between the serum or plasma and other cellular elements of the sample, especially for more sensitive testing. However, for some tests, the gel can affect lab results. Remove the plasma or serum immediately following centrifugation for any tubes without gel separator additive. Removal can be done with aliquoting, transferring the plasma or serum via a pipette to an aliquot tube for analysis.

Lavender topped tubes contain EDTA, an anticoagulant used for hematology analysis, which focuses on testing for blood-related disorders, including CBC (complete blood count) test, which can test for anemia, leukemia, and other conditions. Fill EDTA (lavender) tubes enough to have the correct ratio of blood to anticoagulant. After collecting the blood, invert the tube eight to ten times so that blood mixes well with the additive.

If the collection tube has no additive, there is no need to invert or mix. Just keep the tube in a vertical position to avoid disturbing the content.

Pink tubes must be spun down in the centrifuge to separate the cells from the plasma adequately. This way, both the plasma and the cells can be analyzed.

Other tubes that must be centrifuged immediately include light green, pearl, and orange. Invert the light green and pearl tubes eight to ten times, so the blood does not clot. As for orange tubes, they contain thrombin-based clot activator additives. The tubes are silica-coated, which, combined with the additive, speeds up blood clotting to five minutes for high-priority tests that are required ASAP.

After centrifugation, the separated serum will often appear red or milky. The red serum is usually due to in vitro hemolysis when damaged red blood cells in the test tube leak hemoglobin (which causes the red coloration) into surrounding substances.

Common errors phlebotomists must look out for:

- Incorrect order of draw
- Misidentification of the patient
- Misidentification of the blood sample
- Hemoconcentration

If the serum does not clot before centrifugation, it can lead to fibrin forming in the sample. Thus, the sample is not useable. For plasma testing, collect samples with blue-topped tubes and light green tubes. Centrifuge all samples for serum or plasma as soon as possible because the cells can change the chemical composition of the plasma or serum, yielding inaccurate lab results. Thus, process such samples within 2 hours after collecting.

Blood samples should not stay at room temperature for more than eight hours. To store them, refrigerate at 2-8 degrees Celsius for no longer than a week.

Aliquoting

Aliquoting is the process of extracting serum physically from the blood sample after centrifuging the tube. Because serology is a temperature-sensitive lab test, aliquoting right after separation of the sample contents reduces the risk of ruining the serum.

Use the following equipment during aliquoting:

- Pipettes
- Vortex mixture
- Cryovials (polypropylene vials)
- Cryostorage box
- Tube racks
- Sample Labels
- Benchtop receptacle
- 10% bleach solution
- Paper towels
- Gloves
- Clean lab coat

Aliquaoting is a very repetitive task. Keep all equipment nearby at the workstation. First, place tubes in the order they must be aliquoted. Uncap the lids of the empty cryovials, and place them either on a paper towel or in a Ziploc bag (if you are doing many samples at once). The cryovials should be upright in a rack. With the non-dominant hand, take the pipette, squeeze the bulb, dip it into the first sample so that the tip is in the liquid, and let go of the pressure gradually, so the liquid is sucked into the pipette. Then, transfer the pipette to the first cryovial and squeeze the bulb again to fill the vial with the collected sample. Fill up each cryovial three-quarters of the way, as filling it to the top can lead to cracks in the cap upon freezing. Once filled, cap the samples and cap the aliquot samples using alternating caps. Add sticker labels to the vials and place them into the cryostorage box.

Handling, Storage, Transportation, and Disposal of Specimens

During processing, phlebotomists' handling specimens is critical to lab result accuracy. One of the crucial things to avoid is hemolysis when blood cells let specific analytes (K, ALT, AST, LD) go into the surrounding sample liquid. This not only dilutes the plasma but also causes results to reflect false high concentrations of such analytes.

Patient Identification

Misidentification is one of the most common issues that affect lab results or a patient's overall health. When labeling blood containers, do so while in the patient's presence. Use at least two patent identifiers, which can be the patient's full name, birth date, or medical record number.

When choosing containers for the blood draw, use the proper containers according to the order lab test. Each test will need a container with a particular additive, be it an anticoagulant, coagulant-activator, or preservatives. Medical facilities tend to have a guidebook or catalog explaining the containers used for which tests.

Samples should reach the lab as soon as possible, within two hours. Many components and analytes in blood samples can be unstable if left at room temperature for too long. Avoid collecting extra blood samples "just in case," as this can be dangerous for the patient and may become useless if kept out for too long.

Specimens may be rejected due to the following reasons:

1. QNS: Quantity Not Sufficient
2. Clotted Additive: Not Inverted
3. Visible Hemolysis
4. Not protected from light or temperature
5. Incorrect tube
6. Unlabeled or mislabeled

Storage

Keep all lab samples stored at the following temperature (in Celsius):

- Room temperature: 20-25 °C
- Refrigerated: 2-8 °C
- Frozen: -20°C or less

Some specimens require special handling since they are more sensitive to temperature and light, which could affect the analysis. For example, analyses for metabolic processes like ABG, Ammonia, Glucagon, and Parathyroid must be kept chilled in crushed ice.

Some specimens are sensitive to light, like bilirubin, carotene, RBC folate, vitamin C, and vitamin B12. Store these specimens in aluminum foil and amber containers.

Transportation

Deliver routine blood specimens to the lab within 2 hours. STAT Orders are urgent orders that take first priority. When processing specimens, they must be identified, logged, sorted by department, and the lab results evaluated.

Proper transport must maintain sample integrity, be conducive to accurate test results, and protect the safety of the phlebotomist, staff, and environment.

Disposal

All phlebotomists must be aware of and follow strict disposal procedures as instated by county, state, and national regulations.

There are two types of waste: biohazardous waste and medical waste. Biohazardous waste is any biologically dangerous or infectious waste, like body fluids, blood, and any substances that may contain infectious pathogens. Medical waste is medical-relating items that may still be dangerous but is not contaminated with biohazardous substances.

To dispose of waste properly, consider if it has been contaminated or not. Biohazardous waste includes sharps, liquid water, and dry waste, any biologically-collected specimens.

- Sharps such as hypodermic needles, slides, or blades.
- Waste contaminated with infectious human body fluid or excretions
- Paper towels, paper, or other material contaminated by infectious body fluid
- Contaminated cultures or Petri dishes
- Human or animal blood, blood elements, ad other bodily fluids
- Human anatomical specimens

Medical waste refers to any disposal items not contaminated by biohazardous materials. For instance, non-contaminated syringes (without the needle), Petri dishes, cultures, empty containers, bandages with dry blood or body fluids, noncontaminated body parts or animal carcasses, any noncontaminated medical equipment, and so on. If unsure, most facilities will provide clear guidelines at workstations about where to dispose of waste ("Biohazardous and Medical Waste Overview," 2020).

Chain of Custody

In phlebotomy, a chain of custody helps maintain the integrity of evidence during a legal investigation. Everything in handling, storing, transferring, and analyzing a blood specimen must be documented.

The chain of custody is used where lab results are relevant to a potential legal case, like drug testing. Chain of custody is a documentation process that provides information about the blood sample from first contact with the patient to the lab analysis. Such information includes the patient's unique identification, comprehensive labeling of the sample, identification of all phlebotomists and staff members presiding and processing the sample (including signatures), and a historical record of all events. The sample must also be highly secure so that any tampering is evident and easy to document. The sample cannot be processed if these requirements are unmet (Chain of Custody Testing," n.d).

Critical Values for Point of Care Testing

Critical values describe any analyte of results that pass the healthy maximum and minimum limits. They require phlebotomists and other staff to notify physicians and other relevant personnel for the patient.

In the post-analytical phase, critical values refer to the lab results that are out of the average ranges or normal values. In other words, critical values indicate a critical medical condition that may be dangerous. Analytes have high and low critical values or limits. Communicate the results with critical values as soon as possible. According to the CLIA, all facilities should have policies for urgent communication of life-threatening critical values. In most US-based facilities, the healthcare professional performing the blood test will be responsible for distributing results with critical values. Phone calls usually do this.

When communicating results, it is required to ask patients or those on the other end of the call to repeat the critical values. This repetition helps decrease any risk of errors due to miscommunication.

Distribute Results

Obtaining and distributing results occurs in the final post-analytical phase. The sample has been analyzed in this phase, and the test results are distributed. Each lab should have personnel in charge of validating lab results.

Test results for validity depend on a patient's diagnosis, blood collection, storage method, and if any factors may affect results.

Depending on the facility's policies, the test results may be distributed by phone, electronically, or paper-based. Electronic distribution of lab reports is recommended. However, releasing printed format should be possible depending on physician and patient needs.

Key Takeaways of Processing

- Centrifuging: Spins blood samples at high speeds to separate into components ready for analysis.
- Samples for serum testing should clot for 15-60 minutes at room temperature.
- Aliquoting: Physically extracting serum from the blood sample after centrifuging the tube. Because serology is a temperature-sensitive lab test, aliquoting immediately after separation of the sample contents reduces the risk of ruining the serum.
- Handling: Top problems are misidentification. Always identity with the patient's full name, DOB, or medical records number
- Specimens may be rejected due to the following reasons:

  - o QNS: Quantity Not Sufficient
  - o Clotted Additive: Not Inverted
  - o Visible Hemolysis
  - o Not protected from light or temperature
  - o Incorrect tube
  - o Unlabeled or mislabeled

- Storage: Keep all lab samples stored at the following temperature (in Celsius):

  - o Room temperature: 20-25 °C
  - o Refrigerated: 2-8 °C
  - o Frozen: -20°C or less

- Temperature-sensitive specimens: ABG, Ammonia, Glucagon, Parathyroid
- Light-sensitive specimens: bilirubin, vitamin C, vitamin B12, carotene, RBC folate
- Disposal: There are disposal regulations for two types of waste:

  - o Biohazardous waste and medical waste. Biohazardous waste is any biologically dangerous or infectious waste, like body fluids, blood, and any substances that may contain infectious pathogens.

o Medical waste is medical-relating items that may still be dangerous but are not contaminated with biohazardous substances.

- Chain of custody: maintain the integrity of evidence during a legal investigation. Everything in handling, storing, transferring, and analyzing a blood specimen must be documented.

  o Such information includes

    - The patient's unique identification
    - Comprehensive labeling of the sample
    - Identification of all phlebotomists and staff members present in the handling and processing of the sample (including signatures)
    - A historical record of all dated events

  o The sample must also be highly secure so that any tampering is evident and easy to document.
  o The sample cannot be processed if these requirements are not met.

- Critical values describes any analyte of results that pass the healthy maximum and minimum limits. They require phlebotomists and other staff to notify the physician and other relevant personnel for the patient.
- Results Distribution: Test results may be distributed by phone, electronically, or paper-based. Electronic distribution of lab reports is recommended. However, releasing printed format should be possible depending on physician and patient needs.

The next and final chapter oversees the Core Knowledge you must know to pass your exam.

Chapter Six: **Core Knowledge**

This chapter gives a study guide for the Core Knowledge portion of the NHA Phlebotomy Exam.

Role of Phlebotomy Technicians

Phlebotomy work revolves mainly around venipuncture and processing blood samples. However, the phlebotomist's scope of practice consists of several tasks: reassuring patients, explaining technical details to patients, taking the pulse, blood pressure, and respiration, bandaging after venipuncture, sending samples to the lab, processing samples, cleaning up the workspace, and labeling and recording details in patient records.

As a phlebotomist, your tasks may depend on the work facility, whether you work in a clinic, a lab, a hospital, a nursing home, a blood donation center, a research department, or others. Most of the work requires a phlebotomist to be on his feet during their shift, and much communication with patients, lab assistants, nurses, doctors, and other healthcare professionals is essential. Thus, it is important to brush up on your interpersonal skills ("Phlebotomy Technician: Mayo Clinic College of Medicine & Science," n.d.).

Another core responsibility is ensuring safety precautions at all times. To avoid blood-borne pathogens from spreading, phlebotomists must follow all regulations when dealing with equipment. These regulations include proper disinfecting before venipuncture, washing hands regularly, and properly disposing of sharps and other materials. Sometimes, they may need to be ready to offer first aid ("Role of Phlebotomist" 2021).

Generally, most phlebotomy training programs take eight weeks to a few months. Starting a job may also require additional training. Some organizations offer phlebotomist certification, including the American Medical Technologists, the National Healthcareer Association, and the American Society of Clinical Pathologists.

Terminology

Even if not all medical terminology may be relevant to a phlebotomist's daily tasks, it is important to familiarize yourself with the following terms and definitions ("Phlebotomy Medical Terminology (And Practice Test)," n.d.).

- *Absorb:* To take something in, through the skin or intestine.
- *Acute:* Severe, sudden, quick onset of a disease.
- *Aerobic:* Requires oxygen.
- *Airborne precautions:* Guidelines to prevent contagion of airborne illness.
- *Albumin:* The main protein in the blood.
- *Allergen:* Antigenic substance that can trigger a hypersensitive reaction.
- *Anaerobic:* Does not require oxygen.
- *Anaphylaxis:* Life-threatening allergic reaction.
- *Anemia*: A condition that decreases the number of red blood cells.
- *Anesthetic*: Type of drug that causes a loss of sensation.
- *Antecubital fossa*: Part of the arm at the end of the elbow.
- *Anterior*: A body part placed toward the front or in front.
- *Antibody*: An immune protein produced in reaction to an antigen in the body.
- *Anticoagulant*: A substance that prevents blood from clotting.
- *Antigen*: A protein that stimulates the immune system to create antibodies.
- Anti-platelet agents: Medications that reduce the ability of platelets to clot.

- Antiseptic: A substance that reduces or prevents the growth of microorganisms.
- Arteriole: A small branch of an artery that leads to a capillary.
- Artery: A blood vessel carrying oxygenated blood away from the heart.
- Aseptic: Absent or free from microorganisms.
- Aspirate: Drawing a substance in with suction.
- Bacteremia: When bacteria are in the bloodstream.
- Basilic vein: The large vein on the inner side of the biceps is usually chosen for blood drawing.
- Bleeding time: A test that measures the time it takes for small blood vessels to close and the bleeding to stop.
- Blind stick: Doing blood draw with no visible or palpable vein.
- Blood: Red liquid circulates in the arteries and veins that carry oxygen and carbon dioxide from the body's tissue.
- Blood-borne pathogens: Microorganisms in human blood which cause disease.
- Blood cells: Cells circulating through the blood, like red blood cells, white blood cells, and platelets.
- Blood clot: A semi-solid mass of blood formed by platelets.
- Blood count: The number of white blood cells, red blood cells, and platelets in the blood.
- Blood culture: A test that identifies infections in the blood.
- Blood smear: A minuscule sample of blood on a microscope slide.
- Blood group: Blood group classifications (A, B, AB, O).
- Blood vessel: A tube that carries blood through the body, be it for a vein, artery, or capillary.
- Bruise: An injury of the soft tissue that results in breakage of the local capillaries and the leakage of red blood cells.
- Butterfly needle: A short needle with plastic tabs or wings on both sides that aid in stabilizing the needle during insertion.
- Cannula: A thin tube inserted into a vein or body cavity.
- Capillary: A small blood vessel connecting the arteriole with the venule.
- Catheter: A thin and flexible tube that is inserted into a cavity of the body to withdraw or inject fluid
- Cephalic vein: The large vein in the arm that empties into the axillary vein, also known as the antecubital vein.
- Circulatory System: Moves blood through the body.

- Coagulate: When blood clots change to a solid or semisolid state.
- Complete blood count (CBC): A blood test that evaluates overall health and detects certain diseases.
- Contact Precautions: Guidelines recommended by the CDC for reducing the risk of transmission of epidemiologically essential microorganisms by direct skin-to-skin or indirect contact.
- Contagious: The property of a disease spreading from human to human.
- Contamination: Unwanted pollution of a substance by another substance.
- Contusion: A bruise, ruptured blood capillaries.
- Defibrinated blood: Blood deprived of fibrin.
- Differential: A blood cell count that assesses the ratio of white blood cells.
- Edema: Swelling caused by excess fluid accumulation in tissue.
- Embolus: A mass of clotted blood that obstructs a blood vessel.
- Endothelium: The layer of cells lining the heart's cavities and blood and lymph vessels.
- Epidermis: The outermost layer of the skin.
- Epithelium: The layer of cells covering the free and open surfaces, including the skin and mucous membranes.
- Erythrocyte: Another word for red blood cell.
- Fibrin: A protein that is necessary for blood to clot.
- Fistula: An abnormal connection from a vein to an artery to change blood flow.
- Gauge: A measurement used for the diameter of a needle. The larger the needle diameter, the smaller the gauge.
- Glucose: The sugar in the blood that our body makes from food.
- Hematocrit: The proportion of the total red blood cells to the total blood volume.
- Hematoma: A collection of blood outside the blood vessel.
- Hemoconcentration: The blood plasma volume decreases compared to the number of red blood cells.
- Hemodialysis: A procedure to remove waste products from the blood and restore any electrolyte imbalances.
- Hemoglobin: An oxygen-carrying protein found in red blood cells.
- Hemolysis: When hemoglobin escapes from the red blood cells into the blood plasma.
- Hemostasis: When bleeding stops due to vasoconstriction and coagulation.

- Heparin: A complex acid found in lung and liver tissue that prevents blood clotting,
- Hepatitis: Inflammation of the liver.
- Hepatitis A: Inflammation of the liver caused by the Hepatitis A virus.
- Hepatitis B: Infectious liver disease caused by the Hepatitis B virus.
- Hepatitis C: Infection caused by the Hepatitis virus that attacks the liver leading to inflammation.
- Hyperglycemia: High blood sugar.
- Hypodermic needle: A hollow needle on a syringe that can inject or draw out fluids from the body.
- Hypoglycemia: Low sugar level in the blood.
- Lymph: Clear fluid in the lymphatic vessels collected from body tissue and returned to the blood.
- Medial cubital vein: The forearm vein most commonly used for venipuncture because it is generally the largest and best-anchored vein
- Monocyte: White blood cell that has a single nucleus and very fine granulation in the cytoplasm.
- Nosocomial infection: A hospital-acquired infection.
- Order of Draw: The order in which blood samples should be drawn to minimize interference or contamination in testing caused by the carry-over of additives in tubes.
- Palpate: To examine by touch to check for a vein.
- Pathogen: An agent or microorganism that causes disease.
- Peripheral blood: Obtained from the outer surface of the body.
- Phlebitis: A condition resulting in inflammation of a vein.
- Phlebotomy is the practice of drawing blood for therapeutic or diagnostic reasons.
- Plasma: A fluid or liquid portion of the blood.
- Platelet: A disc-shaped element found in blood and is involved in the clotting process.
- Plateletpheresis: A standard procedure by which platelets are separated from whole blood, concentrated, and collected.
- Povidone-iodine: Mixture of polyvinylpyrrolidone and iodine used for disinfecting purposes.
- Red blood cells: Hemoglobin-containing cells that carry oxygen.
- Sclerosis: The hardening of a damaged vein wall.
- Serum: A clear fluid that separates from blood when it clots.

- Syncope: Another word for fainting.
- Thrombocyte: Another word for a platelet.
- Thrombocytopenia: A condition that occurs when the platelet count in your blood is too low.
- Thrombosis: When a blood clot forms in a blood vessel.
- Thrombus: A blood clot in a blood vessel wall.
- Tourniquet: A band tied around the arm stops blood flow below the tourniquet.
- Vascular: Describes anything relevant to blood vessels.
- Vasoconstriction: When blood vessels narrowing of the blood vessels due to the vessel walls contracting.
- Vein: A tube that carries blood to the heart.
- Venesection: An incision of a vein.
- Venipuncture: The puncture of a vein as part of medical purposes.
- Venous: Describes anything to do with the veins.
- Venule: A small blood vessel.
- White blood cell: Cells found in the blood responsible for fighting foreign invaders.
- Whole blood: Blood with all its elements (white blood cells, red blood cells, and platelets).
- White blood cell count: The number of white blood cells.

Aseptic Technique

The most recommended technique for disinfecting the selected site is to use an alcohol swab and wipe with friction across the area. Another option is to clean the area with an iodine solution before wiping with an alcohol swab. Always make sure to let the skin dry.

Blood Components

Whole blood includes all the components of blood like red blood cells, white blood cells, and plasma. Blood is essential to fueling the body by ensuring oxygen, nutrients, and antibodies reach the organs and fight against invaders. It also transports waste to the kidneys and liver and is disposed of. Blood circulation maintains body temperature homeostasis. In medicine, whole blood refers to blood before it is separated into various components for processing and testing.

Complete blood count (CBC): This test allows your doctor to know the number of various components in your blood. Components include the number of red blood cells, white blood cells, and platelets. Doctors use this test to diagnose any infection or blood-related conditions like anemia.

The process of blood cell creation starts with hematopoietic stem cells, which turn into both types of blood cells and platelets in the bone marrow. This process is called hematopoiesis. Where do hematopoietic stem cells come from? They originate in blood, bone marrow, and umbilical cords. In medical treatment, such stem cells can treat conditions like lymphoma, bone marrow failure, immune disorders, and leukemia. ("Hematology Glossary," n.d.)

Plasma: Whole blood is made up of about 55% plasma. When separated, plasma shows up as the liquid part of blood. Plasma is made of water, fat, protein, sugar, and salt, and that is because it controls the movement of nutrients, antibodies, waste, platelets, hormones, and proteins. Plasma clotting tests can help identify or diagnose coagulation/bleeding disorders.

Red blood cells: Also known as erythrocytes, red blood cells are disc-shaped cells that look like donuts and take up most of the blood volume. The protein hemoglobin in RBCs carries oxygen from the lungs to the organs, giving blood its red color. Erythropoietins generate RBCs by triggering their creation, allowing them to form in the bone marrow before entering the bloodstream upon maturation.

White blood cells: Also known as leukocytes, white blood cells take up only 1% of the body's blood and make up the immune system defense team. Bone marrow regularly generates new white blood cells, especially the most common one, neutrophil, which fights infection immediately. As for lymphocytes, the other white blood cell type has more specialized tasks. Two types of lymphocytes exist: T lymphocytes and B lymphocytes. T lymphocytes focus on defending against infected cells. B lymphocytes create proteins called antibodies, which foreign invaders be it bacteria or viral pathogens.

Platelets: Also known as thrombocytes, platelets are parts of cells that serve in blood clotting. If there is a cut or injury, platelets join each other at the site to create a fibrin clot, the first layer of coagulation that offers thin protection over the wound, stopping further blood loss.

Blood Group Systems

The ABO group system categorizes blood based on what antigens it does or does not contain. An antigen is a protein molecule found on the surface of red blood cells. There are two antigens: A and B. Individuals may have the presence of antigen A (type A), antigen B (type B), type O, or type AB.

ABO group systems are important in the case of blood transfusions because the new blood must be compatible with the blood type. If incompatible, the blood type will reject the transfused blood. For instance, type A will not accept type B blood in a transfusion, and type A antibodies will fight the type B red blood cells.

- Type A can only receive type A or type O blood.
- Type B can only receive type B or type O blood.
- Type AB can receive type A, B, or O blood.
- Type O can only receive type O blood.

Type O can be given to any other blood type; thus, it is the go-to transfusion type in the case of an emergency in which the patient's blood type is unknown.

While there are four blood types, each can be RhD positive or negative, for a total of 8 blood types. The Rh system describes the presence or absence of another antigen called the RhD antigen. If the RhD antigen is present, the blood group is positive (i.e., Type A+); if it is absent, the blood group is negative (i.e., Type A-).

Antibodies are also proteins, but they live in plasma and help as a part of the immune system. The antibodies in the different blood types will attack incompatible blood type cells because they view them as foreign substances.

When collecting blood for donations, people can donate if they are healthy, weigh at least 50kg, are between the ages of 17 and 66, or over 70 if they have been given blood in the last two years.

Vascular Anatomy

The following anatomy is relevant to carrying out phlebotomy duties (Aboamer, n.d.).

Antecubital Fossa: This part is the best choice for venipuncture. It is a small depression in the arm anterior to the elbow and includes major antecubital veins that are easy to find. These veins can intersect in various shapes, including the H-shape, A-shape, and an atypical shape. About 70% of the population will show the H-shaped pattern.

The median cubital vein is the recommended vein for venipuncture for patients with an H-shaped pattern. This recommendation is because it is large and near the surface and carries a lower risk of bruising. The second choice is the cephalic vein, which may be harder to locate with fingers when palpating, but will be the best choice for patients with a higher BMI, for whom the median cubital vein is more difficult to access.

The basilic vein is the last resort. However, because of its ability to roll easily and its nearness to a major nerve in the arm, puncturing this vein will be more painful and hold greater risk.

The M-shaped pattern is present in 20-30% of patients. With this presentation, the median antebrachial vein is right at the center of the forearm, often with two branches: the median cephalic and median basilic veins. The median or antebrachial vein is the best to choose for M-shaped patterns. It is relatively painless, easy to anchor, and not near any nerves or arteries.

The median cephalic vein is the alternative and is not near nerves or arteries. Finally, the median basilic vein is available near a major nerve and a brachial artery, making it less preferable.

Forearm and hand veins make up a dorsal venous network, in which the dorsal digital veins flow down to the hand's metacarpal veins (across the back of the hand). Performing venipuncture on hand veins is not the first option, and it should only be done in specific circumstances. Due to their smaller size, hand veins are difficult to anchor and insert a needle into and may be painful. If necessary, the vein chosen should be straight, with bounce. Never touch the veins on the inner wrist.

The veins on the leg and foot are the final resort if all other areas are inaccessible. Before performing venipuncture in such a case, speak to the patient's physician first.

In summary, choose the antecubital veins for venipuncture first and foremost:

1. Median cubital vein
2. Cephalic vein
3. Basilic vein

Cardiovascular System

The cardiovascular system's main job is to send blood and nutrients to the organs. Deoxygenated blood is sent back to the lungs to reoxygenate. The cardiovascular system has two systems: the systemic and the pulmonary circulatory systems. The circulatory system takes blood to organs and tissues, while the pulmonary circulatory system focuses on a circuit between the heart and lungs. Oxygen enters the bloodstream in the lungs, is delivered to the organs and heart, then blood returns to the lungs with carbon dioxide, which leaves the body through exhales.

All organs in the cardiovascular system include the heart, blood, and blood vessels.

The heart is a muscle that pumps mechanically and electrically to move blood through the body. The heart delivers blood to every tissue of the body so that the body can work at its best. It has four parts or chambers: the atria (top chambers) and the ventricles (bottom chambers). First, blood without oxygen comes to the heart through the right atrium, the tricuspid valve, and the right ventricle. When the right ventricle fills up with blood, it pumps blood out to the pulmonary valve to go to the body. It is transferred via the left and right pulmonary arteries to deliver blood to the lungs. The blood then grabs oxygen from the lungs and drops off carbon dioxide to be expelled through the lungs. Then, oxygenated blood goes back to the heart, into the left atrium through all four pulmonary veins, the mitral (tricuspid) valve, and the left ventricle. Once filled, it pushes blood out through the aortic valve, through the aorta, a significant artery that takes blood throughout the entire body.

This cycle, called the Cardiovascular Cycle, is summed up in two distinct phases. The two phases in this cycle include

1. Diastole: In this phase, blood fills up the ventricles. The aortic/pulmonary valve closes, and blood vessels bring blood to the heart before the mitral/tricuspid valve closes.
2. Systole: In this phase, the ventricles contract, which sends blood out. It involves the mitral/tricuspid valve, which closes and allows the pressure within the ventricles to grow until it is greater than the pressure inside outgoing blood vessels. The buildup of pressure pushes blood out through those vessels.

Blood vessels are made up of arteries, veins, and capillaries. Arteries are large vessels that carry blood away from the heart, while veins send blood to the heart. Capillaries are smaller vessels that further help blood reach all tissues in the body.

If anything in the cardiovascular system is not working properly, it can lead to the following conditions: stroke, arrhythmia, heart failure, and stroke. Blood tests can show evidence of these diseases.

Hemostasis and Coagulation

Hemostasis is how the blood responds to a cut or injury, resulting in blood loss. Hemostasis jumpstarts the process of stopping bleeding, saving blood, and repairing the skin around the wound. Hemostasis means "blood standing still" (Cleveland Clinic). When the body experiences an injury, it prevents the major danger of extreme blood loss with hemostasis.

Hemostasis is made up of several phases: primary hemostasis, secondary hemostasis, and the last phase, fibrin clot remodeling.

Primary hemostasis: During this phase, platelets gather at the edge of the wound and start clotting to seal the wound and prevent infection. The platelets act as emergency blood cell pieces that stick together to create a dry layer of clotted blood that stops further blood from leaving. Additionally, the blood vessel that was injured tends to constrict.

Secondary hemostasis: During the next phase, a coagulation cascade occurs, which helps solidify the thin layer of platelets. This stage is when coagulation occurs, using the help of coagulation factors, which are molecules that came to the rescue in waves or sequences, hence a "cascade." Layer after layer of clotting builds up to create fibrin, a stronger glue that holds the wound closed.

Fibrin clot remodeling: During the last phase, fibrinolysis occurs. The clot is remodeled into a fibrin clot reminiscent of its original form before the injury.

Some complications can occur with hemostasis. Individuals may have a condition called hypercoagulability, which means there is excessive clotting occurring. As a result, too many clots will be created, affecting proper blood flow through blood vessels. This can lead to thrombosis (blood clotting within blood vessels). Thrombosis can lead to thrombophilia, which is repetitive occurrences of thrombosis, the risks of which include heart attack, deep vein thrombosis, and stroke.

Other individuals may have hypercoagulability, which means there is too little clotting. This can lead to excessive bleeding, blood loss, and internal bleeding. Hypercoagulability is apparent in conditions like hemophilia, thrombocytopenia, and Von Willebrand disease.

Pre-Analytical Errors

There are three stages in the overall lab testing process:

1. Pre-analytical: The first stage includes the test order, identifying the patient, collecting the blood or specimen, and transporting and processing the sample.
2. Analytical: The second stage is during the actual analysis and testing of the blood sample.
3. Post-analytical: The final stage is interpreting, reporting, distributing the

blood test, following up with the patient, and retesting if the doctor deems necessary.

In this case, the preanalytical phase is perhaps the most critical because it is the part that holds the most risk for error. More than one-quarter of errors cause inappropriate or lacking patient care. Inaccurate results or mistakes lead to re-collecting specimens and additional testing, leading to ample medical facilities' costs. For instance, pre-analytical costs are about 0.23% - 1.2% of total costs, which is about $1.2 million annually that a hospital will spend annually.

Thus, phlebotomists must avoid critical errors during the pre-analytical phase. To do so, phlebotomists must continue to refresh their skills by taking phlebotomy educational classes. Guidelines may be updated to offer updated, better regulations to help reduce error, so facilities should stay on top of that information.

Another way to avoid errors in the pre-analytical stage is using the right equipment for drawing, including needles, collection tubes, and otherwise. If not the "right" ones, then the "recommended" ones. For instance, closed blood collection systems are preferred over syringes and needles. When using wingsets, extra steps are involved when collecting for a coagulation test. You must use a discarded tube to collect blood to flush to maintain a correct blood-to-additive ratio. As for collection tubes, lithium heparin is the most recommended for plasma testing. Anticoagulants like EDTA, oxalate, and citrate have counterions like sodium and potassium, which can affect the results of routine chemistry testing.

When choosing plasma or serum, it is important to consider efficiency and quality. Plasma offers a quick analysis, but the serum is preferred because it is a clean specimen. However, serum takes longer than plasma to prepare for analysis because it must clot for half an hour to an hour unless rapid testing tubes are used (i.e., thrombin-based clot activators).

Moreover, separator gel tubes reduce clotting time more than standard serum tubes. The gel is relatively stable and substitutes aliquoting, allowing for rapid serum/plasma separation.

Most tests can use more than one collection tube. However, the phlebotomist's responsibility to keep up with trends offers a strong recommendation for one tool over another.

In summary:

1. Take continuing phlebotomy classes every six months to one year
2. Familiarize yourself with facility policies
3. Choose the right tools and equipment
4. Follow the order of draw
5. Follow CLSI standard guidelines
6. Contribute to quality assurance

Needlestick Safety and Prevention Act

According to the Needlestick Safety and Prevention Act, OSHA has recommended that all healthcare professionals must:

1. Stay up-to-date with the facility or workplace's exposure control plan.
2. Always document information in a sharps injury log, like device type, brand, location of the injury, and description of what happened.
3. Ask supervisors for assistance with workplace exposure control plans or device regulations.

Documenting and Reporting

Phlebotomists cannot act or carry out a procedure with an intent to order documented by the physician. Documentation is required for any procedure, including a doctor's note or order.

The document must include

- Reason for the ordered procedure, which must be for a specific medical condition
- The specific tests to be ordered ("lab tests" is not enough)
- Signed order or requisition that includes the specific lab test ordered

- Unsigned orders with the specific tests must be in combination with an authenticated medical order that shows the doctor's intent to order
- Authenticated medical record alone can be used, but with specific tests listed

If documented in the patient's medical record, it must include medical necessity. If it is unclear to insurance or medicare offices, the followed medical records must be available to review: physician order, progress notes, lab results, and signature log.

Importance of Verbal and Nonverbal Communication

Communication includes four components: verbal communication, nonverbal communication, active listening, and written communication. Verbal communication is spoken word, while nonverbal communication is based on body language and unspoken messages. It is essential to communicate with patients by showing empathy, respect and building rapport and trust.

Phlebotomists must practice active listening. Active listening means paying full attention to the patient's spoken words while keeping a close eye on their nonverbal cues. In providing a response or feedback, a phlebotomist must ensure they do not depend on technical health terminology as many patients may not have health literacy.

A phlebotomist must ensure their:

- Pace is steady and not too fact
- Pitch is balanced
- Voice volume is loud enough without being rude
- Body language is open and positive, with plenty of smiles and a straight, relaxed posture

Another vital aspect to communication is being respectful of patients' backgrounds, beliefs, cultures, and religions. Understanding these and other aspects of communication is essential for providing proper information for patients, making them feel comfortable, and ensuring successful procedures ("Effective Communication," n.d.).

Professionalism & Ethical Standards

Maintaining a solid code of ethics is a significant part of phlebotomist professionalism. ("NAPTP Code of Ethics - NAPTP," n.d.) The Code of Ethics for Phlebotomists is a nonnegotiable responsibility that includes nine provisions or services they must provide:

1. Practice compassion and respect for individuals' dignity and worth, regardless of background.
2. Commitment to servicing the patient.
3. Promote and advocate for patients' rights, safety, and wellbeing.
4. Be accountable and responsible for the service and care provided and the decisions made in providing the best care possible.
5. Uphold competence in your duties.
6. Maintain morals in the work setting through individual and collective action.
7. Cooperate in advancing the research, practice, or education of phlebotomy, and maintain professional standards in the workplace.
8. Collaborate with fellow staff and healthcare workers to protect patients and maintain health initiatives.
9. Preserve the integrity of the phlebotomy profession by valuing social justice alongside health policy.

While not legally binding, ethical standards must be upheld in all workplace interactions. (MCL Education 2019)

Key Takeaways of Core Knowledge

- Role of Phlebotomy Technicians

    o Consists of several tasks: Reassuring patients, explaining technical details to patients, taking the pulse, blood pressure, and respiration, bandaging after venipuncture, sending samples to the lab, processing samples, cleaning up the workspace, labeling and recording details in patient records.

- Aseptic Technique

  o Use an alcohol swab and wipe with friction across the area. Always make sure to let the skin dry.

- Blood Components

  o Complete blood count (CBC): This test allows your doctor to know the number of various components in your blood.
  o Plasma: Whole blood is made up of about 55% plasma. It controls the movement of nutrients, antibodies, waste, platelets, hormones, and proteins.
  o Red blood cells: The protein hemoglobin in RBCs carries oxygen from the lungs to the organs and gives blood its red color.
  o White blood cells: Also known as leukocytes, white blood cells take up only 1% of the body's blood and make up the immune system defense team. Lymphocytes, the other white blood cell type, have more specialized tasks.

    - T lymphocytes focus on defending against infected cells.
    - B lymphocytes create proteins called antibodies, which protect against foreign invaders (i.e., bacteria, viral pathogens).

  o Platelets: Also known as thrombocytes, platelets are parts of cells that serve in blood clotting. Platelets join at injury sites to create a fibrin clot, the first layer of coagulation that offers thin protection over the wound, stopping further blood loss.

- Blood Group Systems

  o The ABO group system categorizes blood based on what antigens it does or does not contain. An antigen is a protein molecule found on the surface of red blood cells.

- o There are two antigens: A and B. Individuals may have the presence of antigen A (type A), antigen B (type B), type O, or type AB.

  - Type A can only receive type A or type O blood.
  - Type B can only receive type B or type O blood.
  - Type AB can receive type A, B, or O blood.
  - Type O can only receive type O blood.

- Vascular Anatomy

  - o Choose the antecubital veins for venipuncture first. If unavailable, this is the order of veins that should be used:

    - Median cubital vein
    - Cephalic vein
    - Basilic vein

- Cardiovascular System

  - o The Cardiovascular Cycle has two distinct phases. The two phases in this cycle include

    - Diastole: In this phase, blood fills up the ventricles. The aortic/ pulmonary valve closes, and blood vessels bring blood to the heart before the mitral/tricuspid valve closes.
    - Systole: Ventricles contract, which sends blood out. It involves the mitral/tricuspid valve, which closes and allows the pressure within the ventricles to grow until it is greater than the pressure inside outgoing blood vessels. The buildup of pressure pushes blood out through those vessels.

  - o Blood vessels are made up of arteries, veins, and capillaries. Arteries are large vessels that carry blood away from the heart, while veins send blood to the heart. Capillaries are smaller vessels that further help blood reach all tissues in the body.

- Hemostasis and Coagulation

o Hemostasis comprises several phases: primary hemostasis, secondary hemostasis, and fibrin clot remodeling.

- Primary hemostasis: Platelets gather at the edge of the wound and start clotting to seal the wound and prevent infection.
- Secondary hemostasis: Coagulation cascade occurs, which helps solidify the thin layer of platelets. Layer after layer of clotting builds up to create fibrin, a stronger glue that holds the wound closed.
- Fibrin clot remodeling: Fibrinolysis occurs, a process in which the clot is remodeled into a fibrin clot that is reminiscent of its original form before the injury.

- Pre-Analytical Errors

  o There are three stages in the overall lab testing process:

  - Pre-analytical: The first stage includes the test order, identifying the patient, collecting the blood sample or specimen, transporting and processing the sample.
  - Analytical: The second stage is during the actual analysis and testing of the blood sample.
  - Post-analytical: The final stage is interpreting, reporting, distributing the blood test, following up with the patient, and retesting if a doctor deems it necessary.

- Needlestick Safety and Prevention Act

  o According to the Needlestick Safety and Prevention Act, OSHA has recommended that all healthcare professionals must:

  - Stay up-to-date with the facility or workplace's exposure control plan
  - Always document information in a sharps injury log, like device type, brand, location of the injury, and description of what happened
  - Ask for assistance about workplace exposure control plan or device regulations from supervisors

- Documenting and Reporting

  o The lab order document must include:

    - Reason for the ordered procedure, which must be for a specific medical condition
    - The specific tests to be ordered ("lab tests" is not enough)
    - Signed order or requisition that includes the specific lab test ordered

  o If unsigned, the order must include information about the specific tests alongside an authenticated medical order that shows the doctor's intent to order.
  o An authenticated medical record can be used alone, as long as the specific tests are listed.

- Importance of Verbal and Nonverbal Communication

  o Phlebomotists must practice active listening.
  o Vocal pace must be steady and not too fast, the pitch is balanced, the volume is loud enough to be heard without being rude, and body language should be open and positive, with plenty of smiles and a straight, relaxed posture.

Practice Tests

Practice Test One

1. While transferring serum into an isolator tube, some blood splashes into your eyes. What must you do?

   A. Report to a healthcare provider.
   B. Notify your supervisor.
   C. Rinse your eyes with water for 15 minutes.
   D. Disinfect your contact lenses.

2. You are conducting a streptococcal pharyngitis test on a patient. What transmission-based precaution should you take?

   A. Airborn
   B. Contact
   C. Droplet
   D. Standard

3. You observe a glucometer reading of 250 mL/dL. You get a reading in the average range when you do a second test. What may have caused the first result?

   A. You used too little blood.
   B. You used too much blood.
   C. The test strips were left open.
   D. You used the first drop of blood.

4. You are to perform a glucometer reading for a young adult while the patient's parent is in the room. The parent asks what the patient's glucose level is. What should you do?

   A. Show the patient and the parent the results on the patient's health record.
   B. Ask the parent to leave the room before telling the patient.
   C. Write the results down for both the patient and parent to read.
   D. Ask the patient for permission to provide the results to the parent.

5. You are about to collect a blood sample when you find a cracked glass collection tube. What must you do?

    A. Dispose of the tube in a sharps container.
    B. Dispose of the tube in a biohazard bag.
    C. Label the tube and send it to the lab.
    D. Wrap the tube in gloves and throw it in the trash receptacle.

6. What information must be included when filling out a glucose monitor quality control record?

    A. The time that the values were recorded
    B. Daily test results
    C. The date that battery is changed
    D. Physician's NPI number

7. Other than gloves, what PPE should you wear when performing venipuncture for a patient with pneumonia?

    A. N95 Respirator
    B. Goggles
    C. Face mask
    D. Gown

8. After completing a venipuncture in an isolation room, what personal protective equipment should you remove first?

    A. Mask
    B. Gloves
    C. Goggles
    D. Gown

9. If you receive a needlestick injury, for what bloodborne pathogen are you at most significant risk?

    A. Hepatitis A virus (HAV)
    B. Hepatitis B virus (HBV)

C. Hepatitis C virus (HCV)

D. Human immunodeficiency virus (HIV)

10.   What of the following actions must you do when collecting a blood culture?

A. Cleanse the site to a diameter of 1-inch

B. Remove the tourniquet after 2 minutes

C. Palpate the vein after cleansing the site

D. Rub the site with isopropyl alcohol for 30 seconds

11.   What solution should be used to clean a spill of cerebral spinal fluid?

A. Hydrogen peroxide

B. Povidone-iodine

C. Chlorine-bleach

D. Isopropyl alcohol

12.   After receiving a needlestick injury, what information must you input in the online sharps injury log?

A. The department where the injury happened

B. Your full name

C. The patient's full name

D. The recommended follow-up treatment

13.   What antiseptic should you use during a blood alcohol test?

A. Isopropyl alcohol

B. Ethanol

C. Chlorhexidine gluconate

D. Tincture of iodine

14.   At a minimum, what personal protective equipment do you need to prepare to aliquot a blood specimen?

A. Face shield and gown

B. Face shield and gloves

C. Goggles and mask

D. Mask and gloves

15. A centrifuge catches on fire. In what class of fire should this situation be identified?

A. Class A

B. Class B

C. Class C

D. Class D

16. When collecting a sample for cholesterol, troponin, and HDL blood results, in which department should these tests be processed?

A. Chemistry

B. Microbiology

C. Hematology

D. Pathology

17. You collect a blood collection in a micro collection container after two failed venipuncture attempts. Why should you write on the medical requisition form that you collected the blood in such a manner?

A. To alert the lab of a billing change

B. To alert the lab of the presence of capillary blood

C. To alert the laboratory of possible tissue fluid

D. To alert the laboratory that future specimens are in a micro collection container

18. What is the correct way to perform CPR on an infant as a medical professional?

A. 30 compressions, 3.8 cm (1.5 in) deep

B. 30 compressions, 5.08 cm (2 in) deep

C. 100 compressions, 5.08 cm (2 in) deep

D. 100 compressions, 3.8 cm (1.5 in) deep

19. A patient has a wound infected with MRSA (methicillin-resistant Staphylococcus aureus). You are tasked with performing venipuncture for this patient. What must you do once you complete the procedure?

    A. Dispose of gloves upon leaving the room
    B. Dispose of shoe covers after leaving the room
    C. Clean gown before leaving the room
    D. Remove gown before leaving room

20. You are about to perform the third set of blood draws for a glucose tolerance test (GTT) when the patient starts to cry and does not want to extend her arm. What is the best thing to say?

    A. "I will get in trouble if I do not perform the draw."
    B. "I promise the draw will not hurt."
    C. "May I come back in an hour to perform the draw?"
    D. "May I please perform the draw?"

21. Which of the following statements regarding standard precautions for infection control is false?

    A. Wash hands before putting on and after removing gloves
    B. Standard precautions apply to all bodily secretions
    C. Use both hands to recap needles
    D. Resuscitation devices can be used instead of mouth-to-mouth resuscitation

22. Antisepsis is a technique that is used on which of the following?

    A. Skin
    B. Medical instruments
    C. Tourniquets
    D. Wound dressings

23. How often should latex gloves be changed?

    A. Once a day
    B. Between patient contacts

C. Only when torn

D. Every 10 minutes

24. Once you have stopped excessive bleeding, what should you apply over the site?

   A. Pressure bandage
   B. Gauze
   C. Cotton ball
   D. Bandaid on its own

25. The patient may leave when the bleeding has stopped completely, and there are no signs of _____ or other complications.

   A. Dizziness
   B. Nausea
   C. Syncope
   D. Shock

26. What is the difference between syncope and hypovolemic shock?

   A. Hypovolemic shock is not a medical emergency
   B. Fainting is not a medical emergency
   C. Fainting may be caused by pain or emotions
   D. Hypovolemic shock occurs when the needle touches a nerve

27. You are performing venipuncture, and a hemorrhage occurs in a limb. What must you do?

   A. Apply pressure using gauze
   B. Elevate the extremity and continue applying pressure until more medical assistance arrives
   C. Keep the tourniquet on
   D. Just continue performing the venipuncture. The bleeding will stop eventually

28. How long should you scrub hands when washing according to CDC?

    A. 10 seconds
    B. 20 seconds
    C. 30 seconds
    D. 1 minute

29. Where should you dispose of all contaminated material?

    A. A biohazard bag
    B. Trash receptacle
    C. Sharps container
    D. Plastic bag

30. What is the best way to prevent infection and transmission?

    A. Hand wipes
    B. Wearing gloves at all times
    C. Alcohol-based hand sanitizer
    D. Handwashing

31. When disinfecting a venipuncture site, why should you not use cotton balls?

    A. Cotton balls may be contaminated
    B. Cotton balls leave behind small fibers
    C. Cotton balls can react badly with alcohol
    D. Cotton balls can cause skin irritation

32. Alcohol that has not fully dried on the venipuncture site can lead to _____

    A. Hemaconcentration
    B. Hemolysis of the specimen
    C. Infection
    D. Hematoma

33. What is alcohol's purpose in bacterial testing?

    A. Remove oil
    B. Prevent pathogen transmission
    C. Kill bacteria
    D. Provide a numbing effect

34. What is the purpose of povidone-iodine in bacterial testing?

    A. Remove oil
    B. Prevent pathogen transmission
    C. Kill bacteria
    D. Provide a numbing effect

35. What should you use at the venipuncture site if the patient is allergic to alcohol?

    A. Chlorhexidine gluconate
    B. Sodium hypochlorite
    C. Benzalkonium chloride
    D. Hydrogen peroxide

36. What form must you and the patient sign to permit blood tests to determine exposure?

    A. HIV
    B. HBV
    C. HCV
    D. Consent

37. What is required following accidental exposure to body fluids?

    A. Documentation of the accidental exposure
    B. Testing to see if you contracted a disease
    C. Notifying a supervisor immediately
    D. Act as though nothing happened

38.   What is the first priority after accidental exposure?

   A. Medical examination
   B. First aid
   C. Cleaning yourself up
   D. Removing PPE

39.   What is the term for the following equipment: gloves, masks, gowns, face shields, and goggles?

   A. Personal Protective Equipment
   B. Protective Phlebotomy Equipment
   C. Personal Phlebotomy Equipment
   D. Patient Protective Equipment

40.   What PPE should be worn for venipuncture?

   A. Face shields
   B. Face mask
   C. Gloves
   D. Goggles

41.   When should you wash your hands?

   A. Only before contact with every patient
   B. Before and after contact with every patient
   C. Only after contact with every patient
   D. Before and after contact only with isolated patients

42.   What should be done if your gloves are punctured or torn?

   A. Continue and change after done with the procedure
   B. Put it back together with tape
   C. Don a new glove over the ripped glove
   D. Replace the gloves

43. Where should you dispose of used needles and lancets?

   A. Trash receptacle
   B. Return to phlebotomy tray
   C. Sharps container
   D. Biohazard bag

44. According to the Bloodborne Pathogen Standard, what two guidelines must all at-risk employees adhere to?

   A. Personal protective equipment and HBV immunization
   B. HAV and HBV immunization
   C. Personal protective equipment and pneumonia immunization
   D. Personal protective equipment and HIV immunization

45. What organization establishes regulations for phlebotomists to work as effectively and safely as possible?

   A. HIPAA
   B. OSHA
   C. FDA
   D. CDC

46. What guidelines protect healthcare professionals from exposure to body fluids, prevent exposure, and train for handling situations of body fluid exposure?

   A. Transmission and Exposure Guidelines
   B. Bodily Fluid Protection Standard
   C. Exposure Prevention Guidelines
   D. Bloodborne Pathogen Standard

47. All phlebotomists and healthcare professionals must deem body fluids as…

   A. Harmless
   B. Potentially infectious
   C. Normal, something to be cleaned

D. Dangerous only if it touches open skin

48. What information must the sharps injury log include?

   A. Date, time, name of staff involved, description
   B. Date, time, type of sharps used, name of staff involved, description
   C. Date, time, type of sharps used, staff or patient involved (without names), description
   D. Date, time, type of sharps used, staff or patient involved (without names), location, description

49. In the case of a splash risk, what can you use instead of a full-face shield?

   A. Goggles
   B. Face Mask
   C. Goggles and face mask
   D. N95 Mask

50. What independent, non-governmental, nonprofit organization accredits and certifies healthcare facilities to focus on the continual importance of quality of care and patient safety?

   A. World Health Organization (WHO)
   B. American Hospital Association (AHA)
   C. The Joint Commission (TJC)
   D. National Institute of Health (NIH)

51. What organization established the proper order of draw for venipuncture?

   A. Clinical and Laboratory Standards Institute (CLSI)
   B. Center for Disease Control and Prevention
   C. American Hospital Association (AHA)
   D. The Joint Commission (TJC)

52. What should you first use to disinfect a needlestick injury?

   A. Alcohol swabs

B. Hand sanitizer

C. Hydrogen peroxide

D. Soap and water

53. Starting a procedure without consent is considered:

A. Rude

B. Assault

C. Battery

D. Felony

54. What should you do if a patient refuses care?

A. Notify a nurse and the ordering physician

B. Notify a nurse only

C. Notify the ordering physician only

D. Notify a supervisor only

55. How should you obtain patient identification from a conscious patient prior to venipuncture?

A. Check the identification band on the bedside table

B. Ask the patient, "Is your name John Smith?"

C. Ask the patient's family member what their name is.

D. Ask the patient, "What is your name?"

56. How often should laboratory equipment be cleaned?

A. Once a day

B. Several times a day

C. Once in the morning, once at night

D. Once a week

57. What lab test is the least complicated to perform, with results that are as accurate as possible and a low risk of error?

A. CLIA-waived tests

B. FDA-waived tests

C. Glucose test

D. CDC-waived tests

58. What is not considered a sharp?

A. Butterfly needle

B. Glass capillary tubes

C. Glucometer

D. Microscope slides

59. What are the three types of transmission included in transmission-based precautions?

A. Droplet, blood born, contact

B. Contact, droplet, airborne

C. Contact, bloodborne, oral

D. There are only two types of transmission: direct and indirect

60. What types of transmission do mumps, rubella, meningitis, diphtheria, and influenza fall under?

A. Contact

B. Airborne

C. Direct

D. Droplet

61. What types of transmission do tuberculosis, rubeola (measles), and varicella (chickenpox) fall under?

A. Contact

B. Airborne

C. Indirect

D. Droplet

62. What type of precaution is required for scabies and wound/skin infections?

 A. Contact
 B. Airborne
 C. Indirect
 D. Direct

63. What PPE should you use for contact-based transmissions?

 A. Gloves
 B. Mask
 C. Gloves and gown
 D. N95 mask

64. What PPE should you use for droplet-based transmissions?

 A. Gloves
 B. Mask
 C. Gloves and gown
 D. N95 mask

65. What PPE should you use for airborne-based transmissions?

 A. Gloves
 B. Mask
 C. Gloves and gown
 D. N95 mask

66. When performing CPR, what results in a higher survival rate?

 A. Faster compressions
 B. Slower compressions
 C. Deeper compressions
 D. Shallower compressions

67. What is the adult compression rate during CPR?

    A. 60-1oo compressions per minute
    B. 80-1oo compressions per minute
    C. 100-12o compressions per minute
    D. 120-14o compressions per minute

68. Before administering CPR in an emergency, what should you do first?

    A. Check if the patient is responsive
    B. Call 911
    C. Ask if the patient is okay
    D. Look for a doctor or a nurse

69. When can you use hand sanitizer instead of handwashing?

    A. Anytime, the two can be used either
    B. Never
    C. Always, hand sanitizing is more effective than handwashing
    D. When hands are not visibly soiled

70. What PPE gear should you use when dealing with and processing blood samples and specimen containers (i.e., vacuum tubes, urine collections), like loading and unloading the centrifuge and carrying out diagnostic tests?

    A. Gown
    B. Gloves
    C. N95 mask
    D. Goggles

71. What items are disposed of in a biohazard bag?

    A. Gloves
    B. Glass capillary tubes
    C. Used glucose test strips
    D. Microscope slides

72. What is the normal range for glucose levels?

    A. 200+
    B. 160-200
    C. 60-180
    D. below 60

73. On what document should you record equipment maintenance and quality control testing?

    A. Quality Assurance (QA)
    B. Equipment Log
    C. Quality Control (QC)
    D. Protected Health Information (PHI)

74. What happens if the centrifuge is not balanced?

    A. It stops working
    B. It breaks down
    C. It continues working
    D. It vibrates more than usual, with more noise

75. How should glucometers be cleaned after each use?

    A. Washed with soap and water
    B. Wiped with an alcohol wipe
    C. Disinfected with bleach
    D. There is no need to clean glucometers after each use

76. When obtaining patient identification, which of the following information do you need?

    A. Attached ID band, full name, accession number
    B. Picture ID, full name, date of birth
    C. Patient number, full name, date of birth
    D. Medical requisition number, full name, date of draw

77. When drawing blood from a patient admitted for cardiac symptoms, what action should you take when drawing blood?

    A. Ask the patient to sign a consent form
    B. Collect the patient's blood
    C. Receive verbal consent
    D. Ask a family member for consent

78. Which information is required on the requisition form for an outpatient blood collection?

    A. Patient medical record number and bed number
    B. Provider's name and license number
    C. Patient's driver's license number and provider DEA number
    D. Patient's billing information and test status

79. A patient has a history of syncope in previous blood collections. What should you do to avoid this happening?

    A. Place the patient in a supine position
    B. Place the patient in a prone position
    C. Perform capillary draws
    D. Draw from the patient's hand

80. What should the patient do before their blood is taken for a cholesterol test?

    A. Avoid taking any prescribed medication
    B. Avoid eating red meat the day before
    C. Avoid caffeine on the day before
    D. Sit for about 5 minutes before test

81. What should you use when taking a sample for a coagulation test from a three-year-old patient?

    A. Heel stick
    B. Winged safety butterfly

C. Finger stick

D. Syringe

82.　What should you do if an inpatient has an IV in both arms?

A. Ask the nurse to turn the IVs off for one-minute

B. Ask the nurse to remove one of the IVs

C. Ask the nurse to turn off IVs for two minutes

D. Apply a tourniquet above the IV site

83.　In what position should a patient's arm be during venipuncture?

A. Extended fully downward

B. Hyper-extended at the elbow

C. Elbow bent at a 90-degree angle

D. Slightly bent in an outward position

84.　A blood sample of a patient who ate a fatty meal before blood collection is processing. What should you expect to find about the specimen after centrifugation?

A. The specimen does not coagulate.

B. The specimen has a buffy coat.

C. The specimen is lipemic.

D. The specimen is hemolyzed.

85.　Before blood collection, a patient tells you he is taking warfarin (anticoagulant meds). What type of test will be affected by this medication?

A. PT/INR

B. HDL

C. LDL

D. TSH (Thyroid-stimulating hormone)

86. You are taking a patient's blood sample to check for lithium level after a dose of medication. At which level should you collect the sample?

    A. Peak
    B. Fasting
    C. Trough
    D. Random

87. How should you answer if a patient asks you why his blood is to be collected?

    A. The test is critical to determining your diagnosis.
    B. Your provider has ordered cardiac enzymes and digoxin levels.
    C. You should ask your provider about the test.
    D. Your provider has ordered these tests in order to rule out cancer.

88. When collecting a urine sample for a culture and sensitivity test, how should you direct your patient to do so?

    A. "You must collect your first void of the morning."
    B. "You must collect a midstream clean catch specimen."
    C. "You must collect the specimen after a 12-hour fast."
    D. "Collect the specimen 2 hours after eating."

89. What information should you provide to the patient about the venipuncture procedure?

    A. "I will swab the area twice to ensure it is sterile."
    B. "I will use an evacuated tube system to perform the draw."
    C. "I am going to wait 15 seconds to let the antiseptic dry before drawing your blood."
    D. "I will leave the tourniquet on longer, so we can collect enough blood for testing."

90. What should you do when preparing to collect blood samples to track a patient's medication levels?

    A. Ask the patient when he received the medication
    B. Perform the draw at the time assigned on the requisition form
    C. Ask the nurse when the medication was last administered
    D. Perform the draw right after breakfast

91. What type of urine sample should a patient collect for a pregnancy test?

    A. Timed
    B. First-morning void
    C. Suprapubic
    D. Random

92. How should you interact with a patient wearing hearing aids to ensure he understands the procedure?

    A. "Did you hear what I said?"
    B. "Do you understand what you need to do?"
    C. "Do you need me to talk slower?"
    D. "Would you like me to repeat the directions?"

93. How should you check an ID if a patient is unconscious?

    A. Use the ID bracelet only if attached to the wrist
    B. Check the patient's medical records
    C. Ask the front desk who the patient is
    D. Ask a friend or family member to identify the patient

94. What makes an ID bracelet an acceptable form of ID?

    A. Unworn
    B. Broken
    C. Worn around patient's wrist only
    D. On the bedside table next to patient

95. When can you ask the family to identify the patient?

   A. When the patient is alert
   B. When the patient is inpatient
   C. When the patient is unconscious
   D. When the patient is alert but unable to communicate

96. What is a requisition form?

   A. Another name for a consent form
   B. Identification form with last name, birth date, and other information
   C. Release of patient health information (PHI)
   D. Form filled and signed by ordering physician for the lab order

97. All patients are subject to protection under the _____.

   A. Patient's Bill of Rights
   B. HIPAA
   C. CDC Guidelines
   D. None of the above

98. The patient does not have the right to

   A. Refuse treatment
   B. Access the health information of family members
   C. Know all details of diagnosis, treatments, and prognosis of his or her condition
   D. Confidentiality and privacy of medical records

99. What is explicit consent required for?

   A. All medical procedures
   B. Venipuncture only
   C. Only larger, invasive treatments
   D. Only for routine treatments

100. What should a requisition form include?

  A. Only the patient's full name and birth date
  B. The patient's full name, sex, birth date, ID number
  C. Patient's full name, sex, birth date, ID number, lab test ordered by the patient's doctor, the doctor's full name, date, and time of the lab test
  D. Patient's full name, sex, birth date, ID number, lab test ordered by the patient's doctor, the full name of the doctor, date and time of the lab test, and your initials as the phlebotomist

Answer Key

Q.	1	2	3	4	5	6	7	8	9	10
A.	C	C	B	D	A	C	C	B	B	D

Q.	11	12	13	14	15	16	17	18	19	20
A.	C	A	C	B	C	A	B	B	A	C

Q.	21	22	23	24	25	26	27	28	29	30
A.	C	A	B	A	C	C	B	C	A	D

Q.	31	32	33	34	35	36	37	38	39	40
A.	B	B	A	C	A	A	A	B	A	C

Q.	41	42	43	44	45	46	47	48	49	50
A.	B	D	C	A	B	D	B	D	C	C

Q.	51	52	53	54	55	56	57	58	59	60
A.	A	D	B	A	D	B	A	C	B	D

Q.	61	62	63	64	65	66	67	68	69	70
A.	B	A	C	B	D	A	C	B	D	A

Q.	71	72	73	74	75	76	77	78	79	80
A.	C	C	B	D	B	B	B	D	A	D

Q.	81	82	83	84	85	86	87	88	89	90
A.	B	C	A	C	A	A	C	B	A	C

Q.	91	92	93	94	95	96	97	98	99	100
A.	B	D	A	C	D	B	A	B	C	D

Answers and Explanations

1. **C** - If blood splashes in your eyes, you must rinse your eyes for 15 minutes according to guidelines.

2. **C** - When conducting a strep test (which is spread by large particle droplets), use droplet-transmission-based precautions.

3. **B** - Taking too much blood for a fingerstick can lead to a higher glucometer reading the first time, but by the second reading, it will be average.

4. **D** - According to patient privacy protection rules, you need patient permission before sharing test results in front of anyone, even family.

5. **A** - You cannot use broken glass equipment; it must be disposed of and placed in a sharps container.

6. **C** - A glucose monitor quality control record requires info on the date of battery change, daily quality control checks, and results of checks must be carried out, alongside other maintenance.

7. **C** - When performing venipuncture for a puncture with pneumonia, a face mask and gloves are required because droplets in the air spread pneumonia.

8. **B** - When leaving the isolation room, remove gloves first because they are the most contaminated

9. **B** - HBV poses the greatest risk, it being between 6% to 30%, according to CDC.

10. **D** - When collecting a blood culture, rub the site with antiseptic for 30 seconds.

11. **C** - When cleaning cerebral spinal fluid, a 1:10 solution of bleach/water should be used for biohazard spills

12.   **A** - The technician must include the department where the injury happened, the type and brand of the device involved, and a brief explanation of how the injury occurred.

13.   **C** - Chlorhexidine must be used for alcohol tests because it does not contain alcohol).

14.   **B** - You need a face shield and gloves for aliquoting a blood specimen.

15.   **C** - Class C situations include fire accidents.

16.   **A** - Cholesterol, troponin, and HDL blood results are related to body chemistry.

17.   **B** - When failing at venipuncture twice, you decide to use a micro collection container and explain on the requisition form that you collected the blood in such a manner to notify lab staff as to whether the specimen contains capillary or venous blood to contain the correct test results.

18.   **B** - 30 compressions, 5.08 cm (2 in) deep, are the correct CPR procedure for infants.

19.   **A** - When a patient has MRSA, remove gloves first when leaving the isolation room.

20.   **C** - "May I come back in an hour to perform the draw?" Be nice and courteous of the patient's anxiety.

21.   **C** - You should never use both hands to recap needles; resheathing devices exist.

22.   **A** - Antiseptics are used on the skin.

23.   **B** - The standard guideline is to change gloves after every venipuncture and before moving on to the next patient

24.   **A** - A pressure bandage is best for staunching excessive bleeding.

25.   **C** - It is important to check if the patient is experiencing symptoms of syncope before leaving them on their own.

26.   **C** - Pain, and emotions cannot cause hypovolemic shock; both are medical emergencies.

27.   **B** - If a hemorrhage happens during venipuncture, you must elevate the extremity and continue applying pressure until more medical assistance arrives.

28.   **C** - The CDC recommends washing hands for 30 seconds.

29.   **A** - Dispose of contaminated materials in a biohazard bag.

30.   **D** - Handwashing is the best way to prevent infection and transmission.

31.   **B** - You should not use cotton balls when disinfecting a venipuncture site because it leaves behind small fibers.

32.   **B** - Alcohol that can not be fully dried can lead to hemolysis.

33.   **A** - The purpose of alcohol is to remove oil when it comes to bacterial testing..

34.   **C** - Povidone-iodine can kill bacteria in bacteria testing.

35.   **A** - If a patient is allergic to alcohol, they should use a safe, nonalcoholic antiseptic like chlorhexidine gluconate.

36.   **A** - Signed consent forms are necessary for blood tests determining exposure to HIV.

37.   **A** - Document all accidental exposure to body fluids.

38.   **B** - The main priority after accidental exposure is First Aid to ensure no one got hurt by needlestick injury.

39. **A** - Personal protective equipment is the equipment that shields and keeps you safe from transmission of disease.

40. **C** - For general venipuncture, gloves are the primary personal protective equipment.

41. **B** - You must wash your hands before and after every patient so that one's germs are not transmitting

42. **D** - Replace gloves because a tear could lead to contamination.

43. **C** - All sharp objects should be in a sharps container.

44. **A** - PPE and HBV immunization are two requirements according to the Bloodborne Pathogen Standard.

45. **B** - OSHA establishes regulations for safe and effective healthcare work.

46. **D** - Bloodborne pathogen standard provides guidelines to protect healthcare professionals like phlebotomists from exposure to body fluids, preventing exposure, and training for handling situations of body fluid exposure.

47. **B** - All phlebotomists should deem body fluids as potentially infectious.

48. **D** - Date, time, type of sharps used, staff or patient involved (without names), location, description.

49. **C** - Goggles and a face mask should be used instead of a full face shield because they cover both eyes, nose, and mouth.

50. **C** - The Joint Commission is a non-governmental, nonprofit organization.

51. **A** - The CLSI establishes the order of draw.

52. **D** - Always wash with soap and water first when injured by a needlestick.

53. **B** - Providing medical care without consent is assault.

54. **A** - If a patient refuses care, notify the nurse and the ordering physician.

55. **D** - You must ask the patient to provide full identification without telling them their name.

56. **B** - Clean laboratory equipment several times a day.

57. **A** - CLIA-waived tests can get results as accurately as possible while still being easy to perform at home.

58. **C** - A glucometer is not a sharp object and should not be disposed of in a sharps container.

59. **B** - The three types of transmission include contact, droplet, and airborne.

60. **D** - Droplet-transmitted viruses include mumps, rubella, meningitis, influenza, and Diptheria.

61. **B** - Tuberculosis, measles, and chicken pox are viruses transmitted through the air.

62. **A** - Contact-based transmission illnesses include scabies and skin infections.

63. **C** - Use gloves and gown as the main PPE for contact-based transmissions.

64. **B** - The mask is the main PPE for droplet-based transmission.

65. **D** - N95 mask is the main PPE used for airborne-based transmissions.

66. **A** - Faster compressions increase the survival rate during CPR.

67. **C** - The adult compression rate during CPR is 100-120 compressions per minute.

68. **B** - Before CPR, you must call 911.

69. **D** - When hands are not visibly soiled, you can use hand sanitizer instead of handwashing.

70. **A** - You should wear a gown PPE when dealing with and processing blood samples and specimen containers (i.e., vacuum tubes, urine collections).

71. **C** - Used glucose test strips are disposed of in a biohazard bag because of contamination.

72. **C** - The normal glucose range is 60-180 mg/dL.

73. **B** - The equipment log is for recording equipment maintenance and quality control testing.

74. **D** - When the centrifuge is not balanced, it vibrates and emits more noise.

75. **B** - Glucometers should be wiped with alcohol swabs after use.

76. **B** - You need a picture ID, full name, and date of birth when obtaining patient identification.

77. **B** - If a patient is admitted for life-threatening cardiac symptoms, you must collect the patient's blood despite being unable to give explicit consent. Life-threatening situations are cause for implied consent.

78. **D** - Requisition form for outpatients includes billing information and test status.

79. **A** - If a patient has a history of syncope, place the patient in a supine position.

80. **D** - The patient should sit for 5 minutes before the cholesterol test.

81. **B** - Using a winged safety butterfly when taking a sample for a coagulation test from a three-year-old patient.

82. **C** - If an IP has an IV in both arms, ask the nurse to turn off the IVs and wait for a minimum of two minutes (maximum of 15 minutes).

83. **A** - The patient's arm should be extended downward, so blood flows down during venipuncture.

84. **C** - When a specimen is lipemic (meaning foods with fat content were consumed before the blood test), it will appear cloudy.

85. **A** - Taking anticoagulation meds affects PT/INR tests.

86. **A** - to check for a medicine's level after a dose, take a blood sample at peak 15-30 min after the medication is administered.

87. **C** - You should ask your provider about the test. The patient's provider should discuss the reasons specific tests are being performed and the results of those tests with the patient. The technician should instruct the patient to direct all questions to his provider.

88. **B** - A midstream clean catch specimen is used for a culture and sensitivity test.

89. **A** - "I will swab the area twice to ensure it is sterile." Explain your actions as you perform venipuncture.

90. **C** - When preparing to do drug therapy monitoring, ask the nurse when the medication was last administered.

91. **B** - The first-morning void is the most concentrated specimen of the day, and it is optimal to find hCG or human chorionic gonadotropin) used for a pregnancy test.

92. **D** - "Would you like me to repeat the directions?" Be respectful with patients with hearing aids to make sure they understand the process.

93. **A** - Use an ID bracelet only if attached to the wrist.

94. **C** - An ID bracelet can only be used if worn around the patient's wrist; it cannot be broken, unworn, or placed on a table.

95. **D** - Only when a patient is alert but unable to communicate can you ask the family to identify the patient.

96. **B** - Identification form with the last name, birth date, and other information.

97. **A** - Patient's Bill of Rights subjects all patients to protection.

98. **B** - The patient does not have the right to access family members' health information

99. **C** - Explicit consent is required for larger invasive treatment

100. **D** - Requisition forms include the patient's full name, sex, birth date, ID number, lab test ordered by the patient's doctor, the full name of the doctor, date and time of the lab test, and your initials as the phlebotomist.

Practice Test Two

1.   What is informed consent?

    A. Written documentation of a patient's consent
    B. Written documentation of a physician's consent
    C. Clear consent from a patient after hearing a detailed explanation from the phlebotomist
    D. Verbal consent from a patient after reading a pamphlet about the service to be provided

2.   The only time you should get consent from anyone else is

    A. From the parent/guardian if the patient is a minor
    B. From any family member of a patient
    C. From an accompanying friend of a patient
    D. Never

3.   What is medical malpractice?

    A. When you administer the wrong type of lab test
    B. When you do not perform venipuncture properly
    C. When you continue with treatment without obtaining patient consent
    D. When you improperly handle blood specimens and cause a viral pathogen transmission

4.   Patients cannot take consent back once they have given it.

    A. True
    B. False

5.   What is the most commonly selected vein for venipuncture?

    A. Cephalic and median cubital veins
    B. Basilica inner arm vein
    C. Dorsal hand vein
    D. Foot vein

6.   What must you do to find the right vein?

     A. Use your sight
     B. Insert the needle and search
     C. Always palpate the site first
     D. Guess based on general anatomy

7.   What is the first thing you must do if you struggle to see a vein?

     A. Lower the arm to make the vein more visible
     B. Palpate or massage from the patient's wrist up to the elbow
     C. Use a tourniquet to make the vein more visible
     D. Pat the vein site with a slightly damp, warm washcloth for five minutes before palpating the site again

8.   How many times should you mix tubes with an anticoagulant additive?

     A. Once
     B. Twice
     C. Four times
     D. Eight times

9.   A patient must remain calm because high stress can cause the blood sample to have

     A. High adrenal hormone value
     B. High platelet count
     C. High lactate dehydrogenase
     D. High aspartate aminotransferase

10.   What is it called when you assign a unique number for patient identification?

     E. Labeling
     F. Identification
     G. Accessioning
     H. Anastomosis

11. Which of the following is not one of the three primary goals of the Patient's Bill of Rights?

    A. Ensure fairness and equality of the health care system
    B. Address patient problems
    C. Encourage patients to take an active role in their health and well-being
    D. Promise affordable care

12. To deliver quality patient care, which actions should be avoided?

    A. Too many blood draw attempts
    B. Too many punctures
    C. Asking the patient for more details about their medical condition
    D. All of the above

13. Which of the following duties is outside the scope of the phlebotomist's practice?

    A. Collecting a tissue sample.
    B. Labeling samples correctly.
    C. Drawing blood using the appropriate equipment.
    D. Identifying patients properly.

14. What organization gives out phlebotomy certifications?

    A. National Institutes of Health
    B. Center for Disease Control
    C. Health and Human Services
    D. None of the above

15. Implied consent to draw blood from a patient can be obtained by which action?

    A. The patient signs a consent form.
    B. The patient verifies their identity.
    C. The patient extends their arm.
    D. All of the above.

16.   A patient's name is spelled differently on the wristband than on the requisition form. What should you do?

A. Ask the patient to correct the requisition form
B. Ignore the requisition
C. Verify the information with your supervisor or attending nurse
D. Any of the above

17.   Which of the following options is one way phlebotomists uphold their ethical obligations?

A. Good posture
B. Respect for patient's privacy
C. Ability to look at blood without fainting
D. Maintaining a healthy lifestyle

18.   Cleanliness and personal hygiene are important for:

A. Precision and accuracy
B. Timeliness of test results
C. Personal liability
D. Personal and patient safety

19.   The term *right to know* refers to:

A. Not revealing confidential patient information outside of the workplace
B. The patient's legal right to know about the medical treatments and procedures they will receive
C. The phlebotomist's responsibility to understand the lab results
D. The facility supervisor's right to know the health information of employees

20.   What is a characteristic of geriatric patients that may make venipuncture challenging?

A. The veins move more quickly if not anchored well enough
B. The skin may bruise easily
C. They may get tired quicker

D. They are more likely to experience fainting

21. What is a characteristic of pediatric patients that may make venipuncture challenging?

   A. They have a higher heart rate than adults
   B. They have a lower blood volume than adults
   C. They have different concentrations of hormones
   D. None of the above

22. How must you approach drawing blood from a pediatric patient?

   A. You must act that as with an adult
   B. You must monitor and document the amount of blood drawn
   C. You must finish quickly and let the patient rest
   D. There are no special considerations

23. Why do newborns need more blood?

   A. They come out of the womb with a natural loss in blood
   B. They are physically unable to create blood as quickly as adults do
   C. They have a higher ratio of red blood cells to plasma than adults do
   D. They have a low amount of antigens compared to antibodies

24. If a patient has an IV in both arms, how long before venipuncture should the nurse turn both IVs off?

   A. Neither IV is supposed to be turned off
   B. 24 hours before drawing
   C. 30 minutes before drawing
   D. 2-15 minutes before drawing

25. How should consent be obtained in emergency blood collections?

   A. Patient consent is assumed
   B. Do not act with patient consent
   C. Ask for a friend or family's consent in the patient's place

D. Ask the physician for permission

26. A timed specimen is used to measure how the body's metabolization of a substance, monitor anticoagulant therapy, and _____.

   A. Ensure quality of blood specimen
   B. Check if the patient was fasting or not
   C. Monitor changes in a patient's condition
   D. Monitor a patient's stress levels

27. What tests can be inaccurate if the patient is not fasting?

   A. Glucose
   B. Cholesterol
   C. Iron
   D. All of the above

28. A phlebotomy technician is preparing to perform a neonatal screening test. The technician should identify which of the following is the optimal time to perform the test?

   A. Immediately after the birth
   B. Between 24 and 72 hours after birth
   C. Between 12 and 18 hours after birth
   D. 6 hours after birth

29. What information is needed for the requisition form?

   A. Patient billing information and test status
   B. Patient's full name
   C. Test status
   D. Patient's insurance company

30. When should a patient begin the collection of their 24-hour urine collection?

   A. At the second void of the day

B. First thing in the morning

C. After lunch

D. Right before dinner

31.   What test is used to screen for diabetes?

A. Blood glucose profile

B. Basic metabolic panel

C. 2-hour postprandial specimens

D. Hemoglobin test

32.   What is the name for the daily fluctuations in body hormonal levels and chemistry?

A. Diurnal variation

B. Hormonal fluctuation

C. Hormonal variation

D. Homeostatic fluctuation

33.   What is the first thing to do when collecting blood using a central venous access device?

A. Use the lavender topped tube

B. Disinfect the site three times

C. Disinfect the collection bottles

D. Discard 5 mL of blood

34.   How much blood should be flushed or discarded for coagulation tests?

A. 10 mL

B. 20 mL

C. 50 mL

D. None

35. What do the following tests have in common: ammonia, lactic acid, acetone, PTH, homocysteine, ABG?

    A. They all must be chilled right after collection
    B. They are all analytes
    C. They all test for hormonal conditions
    D. They have nothing in common

36. What do the following tests have in common: Bilirubin, Vitamin A, folate, vitamins A, B6, and B12?

    A. They all require serum separation
    B. They are all tests affected by heat
    C. They are all tests that are affected by light exposure
    D. All of them are used to identify and diagnose diabetes

37. What do the following tests have in common: molecular diagnostic specimens, drug screening, and blood alcohol specimens?

    A. All are done only for sports players and athletes
    B. All are relevant to neurological diseases
    C. All are used for forensic studies
    D. They have nothing in common

38. What is the first course of action if a patient has an IV?

    A. Draw blood through the IV
    B. Consult a nurse or doctor
    C. Use the femoral vein on the leg
    D. Use the other arm

39. Where should you select the site if drawing from the same arm as the IV?

    A. Take the IV out and use the same site
    B. Below the IV site
    C. Above the IV site
    D. At the wrist veins

40.   What should you document in the case of venipuncture on the same arm of an IV?

    A. Document that the draw was distal to the IV and the type of solution
    B. Document that the draw was above the IV and the type of solution
    C. Document the type of solution only
    D. Document the site selection only

41.   What should you **not** do after disinfecting the venipuncture site?

    A. Allow the antiseptic to dry
    B. Disinfect it again
    C. Wipe the skin dry with a cotton ball
    D. Choose another site

42.   What should you do during venipuncture if the patient has many severe burns?

    A. Avoid using a tourniquet
    B. Use a syringe
    C. Avoid the burned areas
    D. Use a winged needle set

43.   How long should a tourniquet remain on the patient?

    A. 1 minute
    B. 2 minutes
    C. 3 minutes
    D. 5 minutes

44.   What does not have a risk of hemolysis?

    A. Using a huge needle
    B. Shaking the tubes vigorously
    C. Using a too-small needle
    D. Not letting the antiseptic dry before inserting the needle

45. When collecting a sample to determine blood alcohol levels, what color tube should be used?

    A. Gray
    B. Red
    C. Blue
    D. Yellow

46. What do you add to a sample if it needs to be diluted?

    A. Anticoagulant
    B. Preservative
    C. Diluent
    D. All of the above

47. Potassium EDTA binds to what element in the blood?

    A. Iron
    B. Calcium
    C. Magnesium
    D. All of the above

48. A failure to fast when ordered can impact a blood sample in the following ways?

    A. Increasing its turbidity
    B. Increasing stress hormones
    C. Increasing enzymes such as creatinine and fatty acids
    D. A false increase in analytes

49. How must you anchor a vein?

    A. Place your thumb on the side of the vein and press down
    B. Place the thumb of the non-dominant hand below the vein and stretch the skin tightly
    C. Increase pressure at the tip of the needle
    D. All of the above

50. What is the most common cause of blood culture contamination?

A. Not preparing the selected venipuncture site properly
B. Improper transportation of sample
C. Improper sample storage
D. All of the above

51. What is another name for a thrombocyte?

A. Plasma
B. White blood cell
C. Thrombus
D. Platelet

52. What is a common complication in capillary sampling?

A. Vein collapsing
B. Hitting a nerve
C. Scarring
D. All of the above

53. How many liters of blood does the average human adult body have?

A. 2
B. 3
C. 5
D. 10

54. What can cause the rejection of a blood sample?

A. Not enough quantity
B. Incomplete chain of custody
C. Improper specimen (serum/blood/plasma)
D. All of the above

55. What can happen if you do not allow the alcohol to dry completely after disinfecting the venipuncture site?

    A. Hematoma
    B. Hemolysis
    C. Hemoconcentration
    D. Nothing happens

56. What is the nerve most susceptible to injury during venipuncture?

    A. Median
    B. Radial
    C. Ulnar
    D. Musculocutaneous

57. What do you do if you have attempted blood draw twice without success?

    A. Try again
    B. Wait 5 minutes
    C. Call for a more experienced phlebotomist or nurse
    D. Call the attending physician

58. Which of the following additive should be used for a CBC test?

    A. Lithium heparin
    B. EDTA
    C. Sodium fluoride
    D. Potassium oxalate

59. The patient becomes pale and diaphoretic during venipuncture? What is going on?

    A. The patient has syncope
    B. The patient has a latex allergy
    C. The patient is diabetic
    D. The patient is going through hypovolemic shock

60. What happens if you have collected a STAT specimen but forget to label it with the patient ID number?

   A. The lab will process the specimen as usual
   B. It will take longer for it to be processed
   C. The lab will reject the specimen
   D. Nothing happens

61. What can be used as patient identification for inpatients?

   A. Verbal patient identification
   B. Intact, attached ID bracelet
   C. Driver's license
   D. All of the above

62. What should you do if the patient says they feel a sharp pain down the arm?

   A. It is normal to continue with the venipuncture
   B. Remove tourniquet and needle ASAP
   C. Remove the needle but keep the tourniquet
   D. Ask if the patient feels any other unusual symptoms

63. What does the word phlebotomy mean?

   A. Droplet, vein
   B. Blood, droplet
   C. Vein, cut
   D. Red, blood

64. What is a venesection?

   A. Venous circulation
   B. Blood vessel
   C. Artery
   D. Another word for phlebotomy

65.   An emergency lab test request occurs in which phase of lab testing?

A. Preanalytical
B. Analytical
C. Postanalytical
D. Reporting

66.   In what phase of lab testing is disinfecting the selected site before venipuncture a part of?

A. Preanalytical
B. Analytical
C. Postanalytical
D. Reporting

67.   During which phase does centrifugation start?

A. Preanalytical
B. Analytical
C. Postanalytical
D. Reporting

68.   During which phase is a blood specimen tested?

A. Preanalytical
B. Analytical
C. Postanalytical
D. Reporting

69.   What is the best way to apply antiseptic agents to the site?

A. Use a circular motion
B. Dab a little bit on the site
C. Press down in one spot and squeeze the swab
D. Use friction in a back-and-forth motion

70. What should you say to a patient to know if they have ever fainted before during a blood draw?

    A. "Have you ever fainted before?"
    B. "Have you ever experienced difficulty in previous blood draws?"
    C. "Have you ever lost consciousness during a blood draw?"
    D. "Have you ever felt sick during a blood draw?"

71. If a patient faints, how long should you stay with them?

    A. There is no need to stay with them
    B. 5 minutes
    C. 15 minutes
    D. 30 minutes

72. What if the patient does not regain consciousness?

    A. Keep waiting
    B. Call a nurse or a physician
    C. Use ammonia inhalants
    D. Slap the patient gently to wake up

73. What should you do if a patient's artery is accidentally punctured?

    A. Keep the needle in and remove the tourniquet
    B. Call a doctor or a nurse
    C. Remove the needle and apply firm pressure for 5 minutes
    D. Nothing

74. What colors are blood culture tube caps?

    A. Blue and purple
    B. Green
    C. Gold
    D. Lavender

75.   What is the recommended blood-to-anticoagulation ratio of a tube?

A. 9:1
B. 5:5
C. 2:8
D. 3:7

76.   What if it takes longer than 1 minute to find the vein?

A. Keep going until you find the vein, however long it takes
B. Leave the tourniquet on and use a warm washcloth to the site
C. Remove the tourniquet, wait 2 minutes, put it back on, and try again
D. Try another site

77.   What makes some veins harder to find or more collapsable?

A. Dehydration
B. Low blood sugar
C. Overeating
D. Not exercising

78.   What is a complication caused by blood leaking into the tissues?

A. Arterial puncture
B. Hematoma
C. Fistula
D. Edema

79.   You can only draw from the IV if you

A. Have a nurse or doctor's permission
B. If the patient is conscious
C. If the patient is a diabetic
D. Anytime

80.   What two things can help dilate veins and make them easier to find?

    A. Sugar and drinking water
    B. Heat and cold
    C. Drinking water and cold
    D. Heat and exercise

81.   This feature is a shield that covers the needle and retracts the needle back into the needle cap.

    A. Re-sheathing device
    B. Covering cap
    C. Shielding mechanism
    D. Needle defense mechanism

82.   What is a slowly performed blood draw called?

    A. Traumatic venipuncture
    B. Slow venipuncture
    C. Incorrect blood draw
    D. Intraversion venipuncture

83.   What can probing or too much needle repositioning within the vein do?

    A. Contamination with interstitial fluid
    B. Hemolysis
    C. Inaccurate test results
    D. All of the above

84.   What should you do when conducting a second venipuncture?

    A. Use a partially filled tube
    B. Always use a new tube when conducting a second blood draw
    C. Fill a new tube and pour it into the first tube
    D. Use the same tube

85. What can occur if you combine two partially filled tubes with the same additive?

    A. The blood to additive ratio will be affected
    B. Inaccurate test results
    C. Both A and B
    D. None of the above

86. How many times should you invert blue top tubes (sodium citrate)?

    — A. 3-4 times
    B. 4-6 times
    C. 5 times
    D. 8-10 times

87. How many times should you invert gold top tubes (SST)?

    A. 3-4 times
    B. 4-6 times
    — C. 5 times
    D. 8-10 times

88. How many times should you invert green (PST) tubes?

    A. 3-4 times
    B. 4-6 times
    C. 5 times
    — D. 8-10 times

89. How many times should you invert lavender EDTA?

    A. 3-4 times
    B. 4-6 times
    C. 5 times
    — D. 8-10 times

90. What should you use to transfer a blood sample from a syringe to a vacutainer tube?

    A. Blood transfer device
    B. Use the syringe to force blood into tube
    C. Keep it in the syringe until you get to the lab
    D. Never transfer blood between devices

91. What can lead to a change in the blood-to-additive ratio?

    A. Underfilling tubes
    B. Overfilling tubes
    C. Both
    D. Neither

92. Massaging the site of a capillary blood collection can lead to

    A. Shortness of breath
    B. High iron levels
    C. Hemolysis
    D. Low blood count

93. The results show false high potassium, indicating

    A. Nerve damage
    B. Hemoconcentration
    C. Hemolysis
    D. Hemopotassium

94. What bandages are recommended for most venipunctures?

    A. Latex
    B. Gauze
    C. Tape
    D. None

95. When a patient's lab test must be redone for emergency reasons, what is necessary if there is a missing/inaccurate label?

    A. Another requisition
    B. Emergency release form
    C. Calling the ordering physician
    D. Nothing

96. What type of reaction can lead to fainting or hypotension?

    A. Vasovagal reaction
    B. Hemostatic reaction
    C. Hypersensitive reaction
    D. Polycythemic reaction

97. What tubes are used for serum tubes with gel separator?

    A. Green cap
    B. Light blue cap
    C. Red and gold cap
    D. Royal blue cap

98. How should the blood culture be taken if a patient has an unexplained fever?

    A. 2-3 blood culture samples must be taken simultaneously via two separate venipunctures
    B. Collect 2 sets of cultures by separate venipuncture immediately
    C. 4 blood cultures sets must be taken during the first 1-2 hours of evaluation
    D. Just one blood culture sample, followed by another 24 hours

99. What additive do light blue topped tubes have?

    E. Sodium citrate
    F. Potassium oxalate
    G. Sodium fluoride
    H. None

100. For how long do gray tubes for glucose preserve blood specimens?

    A. 30 minutes
    B. 2 hours
    C. 12 hours
    D. 24 hours

Answer Key

Q.	1	2	3	4	5	6	7	8	9	10
A.	C	A	C	B	A	C	B	D	A	C

Q.	11	12	13	14	15	16	17	18	19	20
A.	D	D	A	D	C	C	B	D	B	A

Q.	21	22	23	24	25	26	27	28	29	30
A.	B	B	C	D	A	C	D	B	A	A

Q.	31	32	33	34	35	36	37	38	39	40
A.	C	A	D	B	A	C	C	D	B	A

Q.	41	42	43	44	45	46	47	48	49	50
A.	C	C	A	A	A	C	B	A	B	A

Q.	51	52	53	54	55	56	57	58	59	60
A.	D	D	C	D	B	A	C	B	A	C

Q.	61	62	63	64	65	66	67	68	69	70
A.	D	B	C	D	A	A	A	B	D	B

Q.	71	72	73	74	75	76	77	78	79	80
A.	C	B	C	A	A	C	A	B	A	D

Q.	81	82	83	84	85	86	87	88	89	90
A.	A	C	B	B	C	A	C	D	D	A

Q.	91	92	93	94	95	96	97	98	99	100
A.	C	C	B	A	B	A	C	A	A	D

Answers and Explanations

1.   **C** - Informed consent is when the patient can make an informed decision after hearing a clear explanation of the procedure from the phlebotomist.

2.   **A** - Only in the case of a minor can anyone in a patient's family provide consent, and it must be a parent or guardian.

3.   **C** - Medical malpractice is when a healthcare professional continues to provide a medical service without patient consent.

4.   **B** - False. Patents have the right to take back their consent after giving it.

5.   **A** - The cephalic and median cubital veins are the two most preferred veins for venipuncture.

6.   **C** - Palpating the venipuncture site is required. You cannot guess, use sight alone, or probe for a vein with the needle.

7.   **B** - The first thing to do if finding a vein is difficult is to passage from the patient's wrist up to the elbow.

8.   **D** - Tubes with anticoagulant additive must be mixed eight times.

9.   **A** - Phlebotomists must help their patient stay calm because stress can cause an increase in adrenal hormone value on test results.

10.   **C** - Accessioning is when you assign a unique patient identification number.

11.   **D** - Promising affordable care is not one of the three major goals listed in the Patient's Bill of Rights.

12.   **D** - All of the above. To deliver quality patient care, you must avoid too many blood draw attempts, puncturing too much, and asking the patient for more details about their medical condition than necessary.

13.　　**A** - Collecting a tissue sample is out of the phlebotomist's scope of practice.

14.　　**D** - None of the above.

15.　　**C** - The patient extending their arm for a blood draw is one form of implied consent.

16.　　**C** - If the patient's name is spelled differently on the requisition form than on the ID bracelet, verify the information with your supervisor or attending nurse.

17.　　**B** - Respecting the patient's privacy is an example of ethical behavior.

18.　　**D** - Phlebotomists are responsible for upkeeping their hygiene for personal and patient safety.

19.　　B - "Right to know" refers to the parent's right to information about treatment procedures and who is performing them.

20.　　**A** - Older patients tend to have veins that move more easily if not anchored well.

21.　　**B** - Younger patients have a lower blood volume than adults, which may make venipuncture challenging.

22.　　**B** - When drawing from a pediatric patient, you must monitor and document the blood drawn to avoid taking more than is safe.

23.　　**C** - Newborns need more blood because they have a higher ratio of red blood cells to plasma than adults.

24.　　**D** - If a patient has an IV in both arms, the phlebotomist must ask a nurse to turn or clamp the IVs off 2-15 minutes before drawing blood.

25.　　**A** - Patient consent is assumed in emergencies where the patient cannot give consent,

26. **C** - A timed specimen is used to measure how the body metabolizes a substance, monitor anticoagulant therapy, and monitor a patient's stress levels.

27. **D** - If a patient fails to fast, it can skew the following test results: glucose, cholesterol, and iron.

28. **B** - To perform a neonatal screening test, 24 to 72 hours after birth is the optimal time to perform the test.

29. **A** - Patient billing information and test status are needed for the requisition form.

30. **A** - A patient should start collecting the 24-hour urine collection at the second void of the day. The first void should be discarded because urine is most concentrated in the morning.

31. **C** - The 2-hour postprandial specimen test is used to screen for diabetes.

32. **A** - Diurnal variation is the daily fluctuations in hormonal levels.

33. **D** - The first thing to do when collecting blood with a central venous access device is discard 5 mL of blood to avoid contamination.

34. **B** - For coagulation tests, discard 20 mL of blood first.

35. **A** - These tests must be chilled right after collection.

36. **C** - Tests for bilirubin, Vitamin A, folate, vitamins A, B6, and B12 are affected by heat.

37. **C** - Molecular diagnostic specimens, drug screening, and blood alcohol specimens

38. **D** - Use the other arm if a patient has an IV in the preferred arm.

39. **B** - If you have to draw from the same arm as an IV, you must choose a site below the IV.

40. **A** - When performing venipuncture on the same arm as an IV, you must document that the draw was distal to the IV and the type of IV solution.

41. **C** - After disinfecting the venipuncture site, you must NOT wipe it dry with a cotton ball. It must be air-dried.

42. **C** - If the patient has many severe burns on the arm, you must avoid the burned areas when choosing a venipuncture site.

43. **A** - A tourniquet must remain on the patient for no longer than 1 minute to avoid hemoconcentration.

44. **A** - Shaking tubes vigorously, using a too-small needle, and failing to allow the antiseptic to dry before inserting the needle can all risk hemolysis, except for using a huge needle.

45. **A** - Use the gray topped tube for testing blood alcohol levels.

46. **C** - A diluent is a liquid that helps dilute a sample.

47. **B** - The additive potassium EDTA binds to calcium in the blood.

48. **A** - Failing to fast can increase the turbidity of a blood sample, which means it becomes more thick and cloudy.

49. **B** - To anchor a vein, you must place the thumb of your non-dominant hand below the vein and stretch the skin taut because this holds the vein in place.

50. **A** - The most common cause of blood culture contamination is failing to properly prepare the selected venipuncture site.

51. **D** - Platelets are also known as thrombocytes.

52. **D** - Common complications in capillary sampling include vein collapsing, hitting a nerve, and scarring.

53. **C** - The average human adult body has five liters of blood.

54. **D** - The lab can reject a blood sample if the quantity is insufficient, the chain of custody is incomplete, or the specimen collected is incorrect.

55. **B** - If you do not allow the alcohol to dry completely after using antiseptic, it can cause hemolysis.

56. **A** - The median nerve is most susceptible to injury during venipuncture because it is very near the inner junction of the arm, where most blood draws are performed.

57. **C** - If you attempt blood draw twice and fail, call for a more experienced phlebotomist or nurse.

58. **B** - EDTA is the anticoagulant additive that should be used for CBC (complete blood count) test because it best preserves the blood specimen.

59. **A** - The main signs of syncope are a pallid face and diaphoretic (perspiration and heavy breathing).

60. **C** - Any specimen, even a priority STAT specimen, will be rejected by the lab if unlabeled.

61. **D** - Verbally offered patient identification, an attached ID bracelet, and a driver's license can be used as patent identification.

62. **B** - If a patient feels a sharp pain running down their arm, remove the tourniquet and needle ASAP, as it may have probed a nerve.

63. **C** - Phlebotomy means "vein" and "cut."

64. **D** - Venesuction is another word for phlebotomy.

65. **A** - The first stage of lab testing is the preanalytical phase, in which an emergency lab test request can be made.

66. **A** - Disinfecting the selected venipuncture site is a part of the pre-analytical phase because it comes before the sample is analyzed.

67. **A** - Centrifugation is a part of the pre-analytical phase because the lab is not being analyzed yet.

68. **B** - The blood specimen is tested in the analytical phase.

69. **D** - The best antiseptic method is to use friction in a back-and-forth motion.

70. **B** - When figuring out if a patient has a history of fainting during blood draws, make sure not to use words related to fainting or sickness, as they can trigger such a response.

71. **C** - It is important to stay with the patient 15 minutes after their faint to ensure no other complications occur and they are ready to go.

72. **B** - If the patient does not regain consciousness even after about half an hour, call a nurse or physician. Do not use ammonia inhalants, as they can cause an allergic reaction in some patients, nor should you wake them up by force in any way.

73. **C** - An arterial puncture can cause excessive bleeding, so removing the needle and applying firm pressure for at least 5 minutes is important.

74. **A** - Blue and purple capped tubes are for blood cultures.

75. **A** - The standard blood-to-anticoagulation ratio is 9:1.

76. **C** - If it takes more than 1 minute to find the vein, remove the tourniquet and try again after 2 minutes.

77. **A** - Dehydration can cause veins to shrink and become harder to find.

78. **B** - A hematoma is bruising caused by blood leaking into tissues.

79. **A** - Phlebotomists cannot draw directly from the IV without nurse or doctor authorization.

80. **D** - Apply heat via a warmed washcloth or advise the patient to do light exercise for a couple of minutes (i.e., bicep curls) to help dilate veins.

81. **A** - Needles have a re-sheathing device that retracts the needle back into the cap to avoid contact with the contaminated sharp.

82. **C** - A traumatic venipuncture is when the blood draw is performed too slowly, causing discomfort and pain on the patient's end.

83. **B** - Probing the needle can lead to hemolysis.

84. **B** - Always use a new tube when doing a second venipuncture.

85. **C** - The blood to additive ratio will be affected by inaccurate test results

86. **A** - Blue top tubes should be inverted 3-4 times.

87. **C** - Gold top tubes should be inverted 5 times.

88. **D** - Green tubes should be inverted 8-10 times.

89. **D** - Lavender tubes should be inverted 8-10 times.

90. **A** - Use a blood transfer device to transfer blood from a syringe to a vacutainer.

91. **C** - Both underfilling and overfilling tubes can change the blood-additive ratio.

92. **C** - Avoid massaging the site of a capillary blood collection as it can lead to hemolysis.

93. **B** - A false high potassium indicates hemolysis.

94. **A** - Latex bandages are recommended for most patients

95. **B** - In the case of redoing a patient's venipuncture immediately for emergency following missing/inaccurate labeling, fill out an emergency release form.

96. **A** - A vasovagal reaction leads to fainting or hypotension.

97. **C** - Red, and gold topped tubes are SST (serum separating tubes) with gel separator.

98. **A** - If a patient has an unexplained fever, 2-3 blood culture samples must be taken simultaneously via two separate venipunctures.

99. **A** - Light blue topped tubes contain the additive sodium citrate.

100. **D** - Gray topped tubes preserve the glucose in blood specimens by preventing glycolysis for 24 hours.

Practice Test Three

1. What needle gauge is not for routine blood draws, therapeutic phlebotomy, or drawing a higher volume of blood from donors?

    A. 18 gauge
    B. 21 gauge
    C. 22 gauge
    D. 23 gauge

2. What type of needle system prevents the risk of needlesticks and collecting inappropriate specimens?

    A. Syringe
    B. Evacuated tube system
    C. Butterly needle
    D. All of the above

3. What are Microtainer tubes used for?

    A. Collecting blood from finger or heel
    B. Urine samples
    C. Sweat samples
    D. Blood culture specimens

4. Where is the basilic vein located?

    A. Inner arm (anterior of elbow joint)
    B. The lateral side of the arm
    C. The medial side of the arm
    D. Near the hand, wrist, or thumb

5. Why should you not tap the site when palpating?

    A. It can lead to hematoma
    B. It can cause the vein to shrink
    C. It may lead to arterial damage

D. There is nothing wrong with tapping the site

6. What do you do if you accidentally probe a nerve with the needle?

A. Take the needle out immediately
B. There is no issue; continue with the blood draw
C. Remove the tourniquet
D. Move the needle away and reposition to find the vein

7. When should you label a patient's specimen?

A. Before drawing blood
B. After collecting the blood
C. At the end of the day
D. None of the above

8. Can you disclose a patient's lab result to a nurse?

A. Yes
B. No

9. You apply the tourniquet on a patient, and small reddish brown spots appear below. What are these called?

A. Rash
B. Burst blood vessels
C. Petechiae
D. Measles

10. What can cause hemolysis?

A. Shaking the collection tube too hard
B. Not shaking or inverting the collection tube
C. Letting the blood specimen coagulate
D. Using the wrong collection tube

11. How do you correctly insert a needle?

    A. Insert until you feel a change in resistance (becomes easier to slip inside)
    B. Insert until it is in
    C. Insert and wiggle to probe for a vein
    D. None of the above

12. What are areas of a diabetic patient more susceptible to infection?

    A. Leg or foot
    B. Hands or fingers
    C. Arms
    D. Ears

13. What is the best equipment to use for collecting from an older patient with collapsable veins?

    A. A syringe
    B. Butterfly collection system with an ETS tube
    C. Fingerstick
    D. An intravenous injection needle

14. From where should you collect blood from a ten-month-old infant for a routine CBC?

    A. Fingers
    B. Ears
    C. Hand veins
    D. Either heel

15. When doing a skin puncture, what color tubes should be used for WBC, RBC, glucose, and electrolyte tests?

    A. Lavender and red
    B. Lavender and Blue
    C. Blue and Red
    D. Light blue and Blue

16. What should you ask your patient before collecting blood for a metabolite pane?

    A. "When was the last time you ate?"
    B. "What was the last thing you ate?"
    C. "When was the last time you peed?"
    D. "Do you have a history of fainting?"

17. What is the name for a protein that prompts the creation of antibodies?

    A. Platelet
    B. Antihemophilic factor
    C. Antigen
    D. Capillary

18. What is the purpose of the CDC's Contact Precautions?

    A. To ensure lab results are as accurate as possible
    B. To reduce the risk of spreading bacteria via direct or indirect contact
    C. To reduce contact between patients and staff
    D. To reduce contact between lab equipment and staff

19. What protein is essential to the formation of blood clots?

    A. Fibrin
    B. Hemoglobin
    C. Antigens
    D. Antibodies

20. Where are blood cells and platelets created in the body?

    A. Pulmonary artery
    B. The heart
    C. The liver
    D. Bone marrow

21. What type of lymphocyte is in charge of creating antibodies to protect against foreign pathogens.

    A. T lymphocytes
    B. Thrombocytes
    C. B lymphocytes
    D. Leukocytes

22. What occurs during the diastole phase of the cardiovascular cycle?

    A. Blood from the body fills the ventricles
    B. Blood goes to the lungs to become oxygenated
    C. Ventricles contract; the pressure is pushing blood out
    D. Carbon dioxide leaves the body through exhaling

23. A pediatric patient weighs 15.4 kg. What is the maximum volume of blood to draw during a venipuncture session?

    A. 2.5 mL
    B. 5 mL
    C. 10 mL
    D. 20 mL

24. What must you do when preparing a peripheral blood slide from a capillary puncture?

    A. Touch the slide to the second drop of blood
    B. Pipette the blood onto the slide's center
    C. Touch the slide to the first drop of blood
    D. Pipette the blood 1 in from the end of the slide

25. What should you do when carrying out two blood culture collections for a patient?

    A. Collect one set from the antecubital region and the other from the ventral part of the patient's hand
    B. Collect one set from the capillary vein and one from the antecubital vein

C. Collect both sets from the same site within four hours

D. Collect one culture from the patient's left arm and the other from a different site on the same arm

26. How should you verify if a forensic specimen matches the requisition form?

A. County clerk number

B. Statute of limitations

C. Case number

D. Attorney's name

27. Which of the following tests can be used when collecting a peripheral blood smear from a patient?

A. Sedimentation rate (ESR) test

B. WBC differential test

C. Blood culture

D. Arterial blood gas (ABG) test

28. How should you complete the screening card when collecting capillary blood for neonatal analysis?

A. Place many small drops on each side of the card

B. Layer several drops on the printed

C. Touch the paper to a drop of blood to saturate each printed circle of the card

D. Smear the blood onto the printed circles of the card

29. Which of the following patients can donate blood?

A. A 65-year-old patient weighing 54.4 kg

B. A 15-year-old patient who weighs 61.2 kg

C. A 20-year-old patient who 47.6 kg

D. A 67-year-old patient who weighs 44.4 kg

30.   Which of the following blood types is a universal recipient?

    A. A
    B. B
    C. AB
    D. O

31.   What blood collection amounts are recommended for a 3-year-old child weighing 15.9 kg?

    A. 40 mL
    B. 80 mL
    C. 100 mL
    D. 200 mL

32.   How much blood volume does an infant weighing 3 kg have?

    A. 60-150 mL
    B. 100-200 mL
    C. 240-330 mL
    D. 150 to 240 mL

33.   Which statements should you say when instructing a patient about performing a pregnancy test?

    A. Collect urine after fasting for 8 hours
    B. Collect first urine sample of the morning
    C. Collect your last urine sample of the day
    D. Collect your urine after a meal

34.   When instructing a patient about collecting a sputum specimen, what statement should you say?

    A. Provide the specimen in the morning before eating and drinking.
    B. Provide the specimen in the evening before eating dinner
    C. Provide the specimen in the morning after eating and drinking
    D. Provide the specimen in the evening after dinner

35. What additive should be used for peripheral blood smear for WBC count?

   A. Sodium Fluoride
   B. EDTA
   C. Sodium Citrate
   D. Heparin

36. What blood type should a patient with type O receive for a blood transfusion?

   A. Type A
   B. Type B
   C. Type AB
   D. Type O

37. You are going to collect blood cultures, PTT, and testosterone levels. In what order should the following collection tubes be used?

   A. Yellow topped tube, blue topped tube, red topped tube
   B. Yellow topped tube, red topped tube, blue topped tube
   C. Blue topped tube, red topped tube, yellow topped tube
   D. Blue topped tube, yellow topped tube, red topped tube

38. What should you say when explaining to a patient how to collect an at-home fecal specimen?

   A. Refrigerate the fecal sample after collection
   B. Do not mix urine with the fecal sample
   C. Avoid washing the outside of the container following collection
   D. Scoop the fecal sample from the toilet into the container

39. Where should the neonatal screening card be dried after blood spot collection?

   A. Place the card in direct sunlight
   B. Allow the card to dry for one hour
   C. Place the card on a flat dry surface

D. Stack cards on a drying rack

40. Which of the following measurements shows that a donor can provide blood?

   A. Pulse rate 40/min
   B. Diastolic blood pressure 110 mm Hg
   C. Temperature 37.7 C (99.8F)
   D. Hematocrit level 42%

41. A phlebotomy technician uses a syringe to collect a blood culture set, a PTT, and a CBC test. Which of the following should the technician identify as the proper draw order?

   A. Anaerobic bottle, aerobic bottle, light-blue-topped tube, EDTA.
   B. EDTA, anaerobic bottle, aerobic bottle, light-blue-topped tube
   C. Aerobic bottle, light-blue-topped tube, EDTA, anaerobic bottle
   D. None of the above

42. Which type of collection is a priority?

   A. STAT collection
   B. Diabetes test
   C. Profile
   D. Analyte panel

43. By what order should patient blood specimens be collected?

   A. Fasting, drug level, glucose tolerance testing
   B. Fasting, glucose tolerance testing, drug level
   C. Drug level, glucose tolerance testing, fasting
   D. Drug level, fasting, glucose tolerance testing

44. What is the lowest a drug gets in the bloodstream before the next dose?

   A. Peak level
   B. Trough level

C. Second dose

D. Half-time

45. When does peak level occur in therapeutic drug monitoring?

A. Five minutes after the patient takes the drug

B. 30-60 minutes after the patient takes the drug

C. After lunch

D. Right before taking the next dose

46. What must the patient do before an oral glucose tolerance test?

A. Avoid coffee, smoking, and other substances

B. Sleep 7-8 hours

C. Avoid eating anything with sugar

D. Fast for 12 hours before the test

47. What should be used to clean the tops of blood collection tubes?

A. Alcohol

B. Iodine

C. Chlorhexidine

D. Water and soap

48. PKU tests are performed using _____?

A. Arterial blood

B. Bilirubin specimens

C. Skin puncture blood

D. BUN analysis

49. What information can a blood smear provide?

A. Shape and amount of all blood cells

B. The health of red blood cells

C. The presence of lymphocytes

D. The presence of anemia

50. The following conditions are related to which blood cell: HIV, leukemia, lymphoma?

    A. Red blood cells
    B. White blood cells
    C. Platelets
    D. Plasma

51. The following conditions are related to what blood cells: thrombocytopenia and myeloproliferative disorders.

    A. Red blood cells
    B. White blood cells
    C. Platelets
    D. Plasma

52. The following conditions are related to which blood cell: Sick cell anemia, polycythemia rubra vera, iron deficiency?

    A. Red blood cells
    B. White blood cells
    C. Platelets
    D. Plasma

53. Before collecting a blood smear, check if the patient takes any medications. Which medication can affect a blood smear's results?

    A. Antibiotics
    B. Warfarin
    C. NSAIDs
    D. All of the above

54. What word refers to the total red blood cells in proportion to the total blood volume?

    A. Hemostasis
    B. Hemocrit

C. Hemoconcentration

D. Hemolysis

55. What is the process of stopping bleeding through constricting the blood vessels and blood clotting at a site of injury?

A. Hemostasis

B. Hemocrit

C. Hemoconcentration

D. Hemolysis

56. What are blood clots made up of?

A. Plasma

B. Serum

C. Red blood cells

D. Platelets

57. What is it called when blood capillaries rupture?

A. Defibrinated

B. Contusion

C. Hematoma

D. Ecchymosis

58. What is it called when a vein connects to an artery-changing blood course?

A. Fistula

B. Lymphodema

C. Phlebitis

D. Plateletpheresis

59. What happens during the first phase of hemostasis?

A. Fibrin clot remodeling

B. Fibrinolysis

C. Coagulation cascade

D. Platelets begin blood clotting

60. What happens during the second stage of hemostasis?

A. Fibrin clot remodeling
B. Fibrinolysis
C. Coagulation cascade
D. Platelets begin blood clotting

61. What happens during the final stage of hemostasis?

A. Hemoconcentration
B. Fibrin clot remodeling
C. Coagulation cascade
D. Plateletpheresis

62. What is it called when there is excessive blood clotting?

A. Hypercoagulability
B. Thrombosis
C. Hypocoagulablity
D. Hemoconcentration

63. What is it called when there is too little clotting?

A. Hypercoagulability
B. Thrombosis
C. Hypocoagulablity
D. Hemoconcentration

64. What can hypercoagulability lead to?

A. Hemophilia
B. Thrombophilia
C. Anemia
D. Von Willebrand

65. What can hypercoagulability lead to?

   A. Stroke
   B. Deep vein thrombosis
   C. Thrombocytopenia
   D. Heart attack

66. Which additive is most recommended for plasma testing?

   A. EDTA
   B. lithium heparin
   C. thrombin-based clot activator
   D. SST

67. What is a necessary responsibility of phlebotomists under the Needlestick Safety and Prevention Act?

   A. Document information in a sharps injury log
   B. Throw away broken sharps
   C. Notify a supervisor when a needlestick injury occurs
   D. The Needlestick Safety and Prevention Act does not exist

68. What is a requirement for documentation when it comes to a physician ordering a lab test?

   A. It must be documented electronically
   B. It must include a purpose and have medical necessity
   C. It must be reviewed by the head nurse first
   D. It must be reviewed by the insurance company first

69. Sodium fluoride is used to preserve ____ for three days.

   A. Cellulose
   B. Cellulite
   C. Glucose
   D. Glycerine

70. HIV stands for:

    A. Human Immunodeficiency Virus
    B. Hereditary Immunodeficiency Virus
    C. Human Immunodeffective Virus
    D. Human Immunodetoxic Virus

71. What purpose does the multi-draw needle serve?

    A. Drawing blood from multiple patients
    B. Drawing one sample from a patient many times
    C. To collect blood from multiple patients many times
    D. To draw multiple tubes of blood from the same patient during venipuncture

72. In what order should you remove PPE?

    A. Gown, gloves, mask
    B. Mask, gown, gloves
    C. Mask, mask, gloves
    D. Gloves, gown, mask

73. What makes up 55% of blood content?

    A. Red blood cells
    B. Hemoglobin
    C. Plasma
    D. Leukocytes

74. How many types of white blood cells are there?

    A. 5
    B. 6
    C. 7
    D. 8

75. What color tube should be used to obtain an electrolyte panel specimen?

   A. Green
   B. Red
   C. Gold
   D. Royal Blue

76. What is a pathogen?

   A. A non-infectious organism
   B. A specific type of red blood cell
   C. An organism needed for survival
   D. A microorganism that causes disease in its host

77. What is a BBP?

   A. Blood-Borne Prothombrin
   B. Blood-Borne Plasma
   C. Blood-Borne Pathogen
   D. None of the above

78. How should the needle bevel be facing when inserted into the arm?

   A. Downwards
   B. Angled towards the patient
   C. Angled away from the patient
   D. Upwards

79. What is it called when a group of blood tests must be performed?

   A. Profile
   B. Panel
   C. Both A & B
   D. None of the above

80. What is phlebitis?

   A. Inflammation of a vein
   B. Blood clot in the circulatory system
   C. Swelling within tissues
   D. None of the above

81. What is it called when something is free of pathogenic microorganisms?

   A. Medical Aseptic
   B. Quality Assurance
   C. Medical Asepsis
   D. Antiseptic

82. What percentage of blood volume comprises red blood cells, white blood cells, and platelets?

   A. 45%
   B. 55%
   C. 75%
   D. 15%

83. Infections that originate in hospitals are known as

   A. Neonatal infections
   B. Nosocomial infections
   C. Nosocomial infections
   D. Nosocomial infections

84. What tube contains the reversible anticoagulant citrate?

   A. Black
   B. Pink
   C. Grey
   D. Light blue

85.   Serum is:

A. Neither a red or white blood cell
B. Plasma with the clotting proteins removed
C. A liquid that separates when blood coagulates
D. All of the above

86.   What tubes contain no additives?

A. Red (plastic)
B. Red (glass)
C. Pink
D. Black

87.   What is septicemia?

A. The swelling of clotted blood
B. Blood clotting
C. Blood poisoning caused by bacteria
D. None of the above

88.   What is the difference between plasma and serum?

A. Plasma contains enzymes
B. Plasma contains globulins
C. Plasma contains fibrinogen
D. Plasma contains nitrogenous waste

89.   Serum is used more frequently for testing than plasma because

A. It has fewer antigens
B. It has more antigens
C. It has more anticoagulants
D. It has fewer gases

90. After centrifugation, what is the liquid component of a sample in an anticoagulation collection tube?

    A. Plasma
    B. Serum
    C. Cellular components
    D. Additive

91. After centrifugation, what is the liquid component of a sample that has clotted?

    A. Plasma
    B. Serum
    C. Cellular component
    D. Additive

92. What is the purpose of centrifuging samples?

    A. To analyze the blood specimens
    B. To organize the blood specimens
    C. To mix the samples with the additives properly
    D. To separate plasma and serum

93. What layers are separated during centrifugation?

    A. Plasma and cells
    B. Plasma, gel, cells
    C. Serum, gel, cells
    D. White blood cells, red blood cells

94. What are the un-clearly defined layers after centrifugation?

    A. Serum with fibrin, gel, cells
    B. Plasma, serum, whole blood
    C. Plasma, gels, cells
    D. Serum with fibrin, plasma, blood

95.   What body system notices any internal or external changes and reacts accordingly?

    A. Circulatory system
    B. Respiratory system
    C. Nervous system
    D. Endocrine system

96.   What type of blood cell fights against viruses, parasites, allergens, and other pathogens?

    A. Basophils
    B. Neutrophils
    C. Monocytes
    D. Eosinophils

97.   Where is the antecubital fossa located?

    A. The inner side of the arm at the bend of the elbow
    B. The outer side of the arm at the bend of the elbow
    C. The back of the arm at the bend of the elbow
    D. The front of the arm at the bend of the elbow

98.   What blood vessels flow from the heart to the body tissues and only have smooth muscle lining its vessel walls?

    A. Venous blood vessels
    B. Capillary blood vessels
    C. Arterial blood vessels
    D. Aorta

99.   A winged infusion set is also known as a?

    A. Sharp
    B. Syringe
    C. Butterfly needle
    D. Evacuated tube system

100. What does hemolysis mean?

    A. Hemolysis is the breakdown of white blood cells.
    B. Hemolysis is the breakdown of plasma.
    C. Hemolysis is the breakdown of red blood cells.
    D. Hemolysis is the breakdown of blood into serum, plasma, and cells.

Answer Key

Q.	1	2	3	4	5	6	7	8	9	10
A.	A	B	A	C	A	D	B	A	C	A

Q.	11	12	13	14	15	16	17	18	19	20
A.	A	A	B	D	A	A	C	B	A	D

Q.	21	22	23	24	25	26	27	28	29	30
A.	C	A	C	A	D	C	B	C	A	C

Q.	31	32	33	34	35	36	37	38	39	40
A.	A	C	B	A	B	D	A	B	C	D

Q.	41	42	43	44	45	46	47	48	49	50
A.	A	A	D	D	B	D	A	C	A	B

Q.	51	52	53	54	55	56	57	58	59	60
A.	C	A	D	B	A	D	B	A	D	C

Q.	61	62	63	64	65	66	67	68	69	70
A.	B	A	C	B	C	B	A	B	C	A

Q.	71	72	73	74	75	76	77	78	79	80
A.	D	D	C	A	A	A	C	D	C	A

Q.	81	82	83	84	85	86	87	88	89	90
A.	C	B	C	D	D	B	C	C	B	A

Q.	91	92	93	94	95	96	97	98	99	100
A.	B	D	C	A	D	A	D	B	C	C

Answers and Explanations

1. **A** - An 18 gauge is used in rare cases and is not for routine draws like the 21, 22, or 23.

2. **B** - The evacuated tube system prevents the risk of needlesticks and collecting inappropriate specimens.

3. **A** - Microtainer tubes collect blood from the finger or heel.

4. **C** - The basilic vein is located on the medial side of the arm.

5. **A** - Tapping the venipuncture site can lead to a hematoma, especially in patients with fragile veins.

6. **D** - If you accidentally probe a nerve, take the needle out immediately to avoid the risk of permanent damage.

7. **B** - Phlebotomists must label the patient's specimen right after collecting it.

8. **A** - Disclosing a patient's lab results to a nurse is not a breach of confidentiality because it is clinically significant.

9. **C** - Petechiae is when small reddish brown spots appear below the application of a tourniquet.

10. **A** - Shaking the collection tube too vigorously can lead to hemolysis of the specimen.

11. **A** - To correctly insert a needle, you must insert the needle until you feel a change in resistance (from tough to easy).

12. **A** - The leg or foot of diabetic patients are more susceptible to infection due to lower blood flow to extremities.

13. **B** - A syringe and butterfly collection system with an ETS tube is best for older patients.

14. **D** - Use either heel to collect blood from a 10-month-old infant for a routine CBC.

15. **A** - The lavender and red topped tubes can be used for WBC, RBC, glucose, and electrolyte tests.

16. **A** - When asking for a metabolite panel, ask the patient when was the last time they ate to ensure they came fasted for at least 8 hours.

17. **C** - The protein that prompts the creation of antibodies is called an antigen.

18. **B** - The CDC's Contact Precaution aims to reduce the risk of spreading bacteria directly or indirectly.

19. **A** - Fibrin is the protein that is essential to proper blood clotting.

20. **D** - Blood cells and platelets are created in the bone marrow.

21. **C** - The B lymphocytes are in charge of creating antibodies to protect against foreign pathogens.

22. **A** - During the diastole phase of the cardiovascular cycle, blood from the body fills the ventricles.

23. **C** - The maximum blood volume to draw from a pediatric patient weighing 15.4 kg is 10 mL.

24. **A** - When preparing a peripheral blood slide, touch the slide to the second drop of blood from the capillary puncture.

25. **D** - When performing two blood culture collections for a patient, collect them from the same arm but different sites.

26. **C** - To verify a forensic specimen, check if it matches the case number on the requisition form.

27. **B** - A peripheral blood smear can be used for a white blood cell differential test.

28. **C** - To complete the screening card for capillary blood for neonatal analysis, touch the paper to a drop of blood for each printed circle.

29. **A** - Individuals who cannot donate blood include those under 18 and below the weight of 52 kg. People over 62 can only donate if they have donated in the past two years.

30. **C** - The AB blood type can receive all other blood types for blood transfusions.

31. **A** - A 3-year-old child weighing 15.9 kg can have 40 mL of blood collected, per the recommendation of 2.5% of the pediatric patient's body weight.

32. **C** - An infant weighing 3 kg has a blood volume of 3 kg.

33. **B** - When instructing a patient about performing a pregnancy test, tell them to collect the first urine sample of the morning.

34. **A** - When instructing a patient about collecting a sputum specimen, tell them to provide the specimen in the morning before eating and drinking.

35. **B** - The additive EDTA (in the lavender top tube) should be used for peripheral blood smears to preserve blood cells for white blood cell counts.

36. **D** - Type O patients can only accept Type O blood for a transfusion.

37. **A** - When collecting blood cultures, the yellow top tube is for blood cultures, the blue top tube is for PTT, and the red top tube is for testosterone.

38.   **B** - When a patient must collect an at-home fecal specimen, ensure they do not mix urine with the fecal sample.

39.   **C** - Neonatal screening cards should be placed on a flat dry surface to dry after blood spot collection.

40.   **D** - To know if a donor can donate blood, the hematocrit level has to be 42%, the proportion of blood cells in the blood.

41.   **A** - The proper draw order is the anaerobic bottle, aerobic bottle, light-blue-topped tube, and EDTA. Blood cultures bottles always go first (anaerobic and aerobic, in that order).

42.   **A** - A STAT collection is a high-priority sample that will be the first to be sent to the lab and analyzed.

43.   **D** - Drug level blood specimens go first, followed by fasting samples, and finally glucose tolerance testing.

44.   **D** - The lowest point of a drug's amount in the bloodstream before the next dose is called the trough level.

45.   **B** - In therapeutic drug monitoring, the peak level is when the drug reaches its highest amount in the body, which occurs 30-60 minutes after the patient takes it.

46.   **D** - Patients must fast for 12 hours before an oral glucose tolerance test.

47.   **A** - Blood collection tube tops must be cleaned with alcohol swabs to prevent contamination.

48.   **C** - PKU tests are obtained using skin puncture blood, usually via heel stick.

49.   **A** - A blood smear provides information on the shape and amount of all blood cells.

50. **B** - HIV, leukemia, and lymphoma are all related to white blood cells.

51. **C** - Thrombocytopenia and myeloproliferative disorders are platelet-related disorders.

52. **A** - Sickle cell anemia, polycythemia rubra vera, and iron deficiency are related to red blood cells.

53. **D** - Medications that may affect a blood smear include antibiotics, warfarin, and NSAIDs.

54. **B** - Hematocrit is the proportion of the total red blood cells to the overall blood volume. High hematocrit levels can be dangerous, indicating severe dehydration or carbon monoxide poisoning.

55. **A** - Hemostasis is the process of stopping bleeding.

56. **D** - Blood clots are made of platelets, which are partially developed blood cells.

57. **B** - A contusion is when blood capillaries rupture, also known as a bruise.

58. **A** - A fistule is a surgically-applied interconnection of a vein and an artery to change the course of the blood flow.

59. **D** - The platelets begin the blood clotting process in the first phase of hemostasis.

60. **C** - In the second stage of hemostasis, a coagulation cascade occurs.

61. **B** - In the final stage of hemostasis, fibrin clot remodeling starts.

62. **A** - Excessive blood clotting is called hypercoagulability.

63. **C** - Too little clotting is called hypercoagulability.

64. **B** - Hypercoagulability can lead to thrombophilia.

65. **C** - Hypocoagulability can lead to thrombocytopenia.

66. **B** - Lithium heparin is the additive recommended for plasma testing.

67. **A** - Under the Needlestick Safety and Prevention Act, you must document information in a sharps injury log.

68. **B** - A lab test order must have a documented purpose and medical necessity.

69. **C** - Sodium fluoride is used to preserve glucose for three days.

70. **A** - HIV stands for Human Immunodeficiency Virus.

71. **D** The multi-draw needle allows you to draw multiple tubes of blood from the same patient during venipuncture.

72. **D** - When removing PPE, start with gloves, gown, and mask.

73. **C** - Plasma makes up 55% of blood content.

74. **A** - There are five types of white blood cells.

75. **A** - A green topped tube is used for an electrolyte panel.

76. **A** - A pathogen is a microorganism that causes disease in its host.

77. **C** - A BBP is a blood-borne pathogen.

78. **D** - The needle bevel should be facing upwards when inserted into the arm.

79. **C** - A group of blood tests can be called a profile or a panel.

80. **A** - Phlebitis is inflammation of the vein.

81. **C** - Medical Asepsis is when something is free of pathogenic microorganisms.

82.   **B** - 55% of the blood volume comprises RBCs, WBCs, and platelets.

83.   **C** - Nosocomial infections are infections that originate in hospitals.

84.   **D** - The light blue tube contains reversible anticoagulant citrate.

85.   **D** - Serum is neither a red nor white blood cell but a liquid that separates when blood coagulates.

86.   **B** - Red glass tubes contain no additives.

87.   **C** - Septicemia is blood poisoning caused by bacteria.

88.   **C** - Plasma contains fibrinogen while serum does not.

89.   **B** - Serum is used more frequently for testing because it has more antigens.

90.   **A** - The remaining liquid component of a sample in an anticoagulation collection tube is plasma.

91.   **B** - After centrifugation, plasma is the liquid component that remains in a sample that has clotted.

92.   **D** - Centrifuging blood samples is to separate the plasma from the serum.

93.   **C** - During centrifugation, blood specimens are spun so rapidly that blood contents are separated into three layers: serum, gel, and cells.

94.   **A** - After centrifugation, the remaining unclearly defined layers are serum with fibrin, gel, and cells.

95.   **D** - The endocrine system notices internal or external changes and reacts accordingly.

96.   **A** - Basophils are blood cells that fight against viruses, parasites, allergens, and other parasites.

97. **D** - The antecubital fossa is at the front of the arm at the bend of the elbow.

98. **B** - Capillary blood vessels are made up of smooth muscle and flow from the heart to the body tissues.

99. **C** - A butterfly needle is another name for a winged infusion set.

100. **C** - Hemolysis is when red blood cells break down and release hemoglobin into the surrounding plasma.

Practice Test Four

1.   What can lead to micro clot formation?

   A. Lithium heparin additve
   B. Not mixing anticoagulant tubes well enough
   C. A lower ratio of blood to anticoagulant
   D. Test tube hemolysis

2.   What tubes should not be mixed?

   A. Non-additive tubes
   B. Only anticoagulation tubes
   C. Blood culture collection tubes
   D. All tubes should be mixed

3.   What happens if platelets are activated?

   A. Platelets activate the immune response, sending white blood cells to an injury site
   B. Platelets activate the destruction of red blood cells
   C. Platelet-activation releases hemoglobin into the surrounded blood
   D. Platelets activate hemostasis and thrombosis; platelets are sent to an injury site to begin the clotting process

4.   Routine blood specimens should arrive at the lab within…

   A. 45 minutes
   B. 60 minutes
   C. 2 hours
   D. 6 hours

5.   What is the maximum time limit for separating serum and plasma from blood cells?

   A. 2 hours
   B. 1-hour

C. 24 hours

D. No time limit

6.   What metabolic process should be prevented during handling and transporting?

A. Anabolism

B. Homeostasis

C. Glycolysis

D. Cellular respiration

7.   When performing a mastectomy on the right side, what should you do?

A. Keep the patient supine

B. Keep the patient in a sitting position

C. Avoid the right arm

D. There are no special precautions

8.   Glycolysis can lower glucose values at a rate of….

A. 100 mg/L per hour

B. 200 mg/L per hour

C. 300 mg/L per hour

D. 500 mg/L per hour

9.   What does SST stand for?

A. Synthetic serum tubes

B. Serum specimen tubes

C. Serum synthesizing tubes

D. Serum separator tubes

10.   Which is a sign of a latex allergy?

A. Shortness of breath

B. Runny nose

C. Hives and skin redness

D. All of the above

11.   What does PST stand for?

A. Plasma separator tube
B. Pasteur separator tube
C. Plasma serum tube
D. None of the above

12.   Why don't gel barrier tubes require manual separation after centrifugation?

A. Because there is no need to separate blood components after centrifugation
B. The tests that require gel barrier tubes do not need any separation of blood components
C. The gel offers a physical barrier that prevents glycolysis
D. They do; they require manual separation by extracting the serum via a pipette

13.   For how long does gel prevent glycolysis?

A. 1 hour
B. 24 hours
C. 1-week
D. None of the above

14.   Within what time limit must blood smears from EDTA specimens be prepared?

A. Within 1 hour of collection
B. Within 2 hours of collection
C. Within 12 hours of collection
D. Within 24 hours of collection

15.   For how long are CBCs stable at room temperature for the EDTA test?

A. 1 hour
B. 4 hours

C. 12 hours

D. 24 hours

16. What kind of blood do arteries and arterioles carry?

A. Oxygenated

B. Deoxygenated

C. Type O blood

D. Type AB blood

17. What do leukocytes do?

A. Protect the body from infection

B. Carry oxygen to cells

C. Promots clot formation

D. None of the above

18. During hemostasis, what is breaking down and removing a clot called?

A. Coagulation

B. Vascular

C. Fibrinolysis

D. Aggregation

19. What gauge is a multi-sample needle considered to be standard?

A. 16

B. 18

C. 21

D. 22

20. How do sclerosed veins feel?

A. Cordlike

B. Spongy

C. Square

a. Soft

21. What condition does the OGTT diagnose?

    A. Cholesterol
    B. Diabetes
    C. Heart disease
    D. Asthma

22. What is an example of post-analytical error?

    A. Improper site preparation
    B. Not inverting tubes
    C. Mislabeling the sample
    D. Not using serum separator properly

23. What is it called when veins are winding and crooked?

    A. Thrombotic
    B. Tortuous
    C. Hemolytic
    D. Sclerosed

24. An NP (nasopharyngeal) culture swab can identify what condition?

    A. Whooping cough
    B. Strep throat
    C. Coronavirus
    D. Encephalitis

25. Should the needle be recapped before being discarded?

    A. No
    B. Yes
    C. Only with fingersticks
    D. Only with patients without bloodborne diseases

26.   What error occurs in results when a clot activator additive carries over to a blue-topped (coagulation) tube?

    A. Falsely shortened partial thromboplastin time (PTT)
    B. Falsely low glucose
    C. Falsely shortened prothrombin time (PT)
    D. Falsely high potassium levels

27.   For a lactic acid test, which tube should you use?

    A. Gray
    B. Blue
    C. Red
    D. Lavender

28.   Which of the following are light-sensitive specimens?

    A. Bilirubin
    B. Carotene
    C. RBC folate
    D. All of the above

29.   Which tube should be used for a trace elements test?

    A. Gold
    B. Red top
    C. Light blue
    D. Royal blue

30.   What sized needle should be used for routine venipuncture?

    A. 1 to 1.5 inch
    B. 2 to 3 inches
    C. 2.5 to 3 inches
    D. 2 to 2.5 inches

31. What type of blood test requires a chain of custody?

   A. TDM
   B. Drug screening
   C. Crossmatch
   D. Blood culture

32. When should patients stop taking a medication that may affect a blood test before venipuncture?

   A. 1-4 hours before
   B. 4-24 hours before
   C. 24-36 hours before
   D. 48-72 hours before

33. What does the left ventricle do?

   A. Deliver oxygenated blood to the aorta
   B. Deliver deoxygenated blood to the aorta
   C. Deliver oxygenated blood to the lungs
   D. Remove CO2 from deoxygenated blood

34. What analyte has a higher reference range for a capillary puncture?

   A. Phosphorus
   B. Calcium
   C. Protein
   D. Glucose

35. What can the serum show up as if a patient is not fasting?

   A. Hemolyzed
   B. Lipemic
   C. Jaundiced
   D. Hemoconcentrated

36. All patients must be assumed to be infectious regarding this condition.

    A. Bloodborne pathogens
    B. Tuberculosis
    C. Cold
    D. Flu

37. What is an antiglycolytic agent?

    A. An additive that reduces glucose in diabetic patients
    B. Another name for insulin
    C. An additive preventing glucose from breaking down in the blood specimen
    D. None of the above

38. What test needs the patient to take a 24-hour urine specimen?

    A. Fibrin Split
    B. Culture and sensitivity
    C. Glucose tolerance
    D. Creatinine Clearance

39. What test requires a whole blood specimen?

    E. BUN
    F. CBC
    G. CPK
    H. PTT

40. In a red topped collection tube, how long does it take for coagulation to occur naturally?

    A. 5-10 minutes
    B. 30-60 minutes
    C. 15-20 minutes
    D. 60-90 minutes

41. What is it called when you fail to give the proper standard of care that results in a patient being at risk of injury?

    A. Battery
    B. Tort
    C. Trauma
    D. Negligence

42. What lab department would be in charge of analyzing Culture & Sensitivity (C&S) tests?

    A. Immunology
    B. Hematology
    C. Microbiology
    D. Serology

43. All healthcare professionals must take the vaccine for

    A. HBV
    B. HCV
    C. HAV
    D. HPV

44. How do you handle an arterial blood sampling (ABG) specimen?

    A. Warming
    B. Inverting
    C. Shaking
    D. Chilling

45. How much should you fill light blue tubes?

    A. ½
    B. ⅔
    C. ¾
    D. Completely

46. Where does lymph come from?

    A. Plasma
    B. Tissue fluid
    C. Serum
    D. Joint fluid

47. Which of the following is a pre-analytical error?

    A. Wrong time of collection
    B. Wrong order of draw
    C. Wrong technique
    D. Light exposure

48. What type of specimen is necessary for diurnal variation of cortisol?

    A. Therapeutic
    B. Timed
    C. Blood culture
    D. Fasting

49. Red blood cells are called:

    A. Thrombocytes
    B. Leukocytes
    C. Phagocytes
    D. Erythrocytes

50. The following tests revolve around which organ: ALP, AST, ALT, GTT, bilirubin?

    A. Liver
    B. Kidney
    C. Spleen
    D. Heart

51. Which tube can be used to collect blood for a type and crossmatch?

    A. ETS Gray top
    B. Pink top EDTA
    C. Royal Blue top
    D. Serum separator tube

52. Which tube is drawn last in a standard venipuncture procedure?

    A. Blood culture tube
    B. Light-blue
    C. Red
    D. Lavender

53. Which of the following specimens are least likely to require special handling?

    A. Bilirubin and Folate
    B. Cholesterol and Uric Acid
    C. Gastrin and Lactic Acid
    D. Homocystine and renin

54. Performing repeated venipunctures in the same site can lead to...

    A. Phlebitis
    B. Thrombus
    C. Hemolysis
    D. Petechiae

55. What hormone indicated a positive pregnancy test?

    A. GH
    B. ACTH
    C. HCG
    D. TSH

56.   What is the first link in the chain of infection?

    A. Agent
    B. Portal of exit
    C. Susceptible host
    D. None of the above

57.   Which is not a reason for failure to collect blood?

    A. Tube lost vacuum
    B. The bevel of the needle against the vein side
    C. Needle not entirely in the vein
    D. The patient drank too much water

58.   Which test is NOT a light-sensitive test?

    A. Bilirubin
    B. Beta-carotene
    C. Porphyrins
    D. Ammonia

59.   When does the cortisol hormone peak?

    A. Morning
    B. Afternoon
    C. Evening
    D. Midnight

60.   What is a sputum specimen used to diagnose?

    A. H. pylori
    B. Meningitis
    C. Tuberculosis
    D. Diptheria

61.   What additive does a pink tube contain?

    A. Heparin
    B. EDTA
    C. SPS
    D. ADP

62.   Why is glycolysis faster in newborns?

    A. Because they have less blood
    B. Because they have a faster heart rate
    C. Because they have a lower blood pressure
    D. Because they have a higher metabolism

63.   Which represents the proper order of blood flow?

    A. From arteries to veins to capillaries
    B. From arterioles to capillaries to venules
    C. From capillaries to arterioles to arteries
    D. From veins to venules to capillaries

64.   Which is used for PT and PTT?

    A. Red top
    B. Green top
    C. Light blue top
    D. Gray top

65.   What causes vacuum tubes to fill with blood?

    A. Arterial blood pressure
    B. Patient fist pumping
    C. Tourniquet pressure
    D. Tube vacuum

66. What special consideration should be provided when it comes to veni-puncture on newborns?

    A. Use protective restraints when necessary
    B. Ensuring warmth
    C. Provide a protective environment
    D. Monitor the total volume of blood draw

67. What does the presence of petechiae indicate?

    A. Blood pressure irregularities
    B. Possible infectious disease
    C. Clotting problems
    D. Potential inflammation

68. Where is fibrinogen found?

    A. Whole blood
    B. Plasma
    C. Serum
    D. Bone marrow

69. What body system supplies oxygen to the body and includes cilia, tiny filters that keep out invaders?

    A. Respiratory system
    B. Circulatory system
    C. Digestive system
    D. Endocrine system

70. When using a syringe, you should avoid pulling too quickly on the plunger or pushing it forcefully when transferring blood from the syringe to the container. Why is this?

    A. To prevent hemolysis
    B. To prevent a needle stick accident
    C. To avoid adulteration of the specimen

D. To prevent bacterial contamination

71. What is not a requirement for a quality specimen?

A. Non-hemolyzed
B. Non-clotted specimen (with anticoagulant additive)
C. Must be transported to a lab within 2 hours of collection
D. Right patient, right tube, right test, right label

72. When interacting with the patient, the phlebotomist must explain the process calmly and relaxedly, maintain eye contact, avoid interrupting or paraphrasing, and allow the patient to ask questions with close attention. What is this called?

A. Negative body language
B. Active listening
C. Non-verbal communication
D. B and C

73. What is an incident report for?

A. For reporting an incident
B. For telling on another staff member anonymously
C. To admit malpractice in writing
D. To get the story in before the patient does

74. What is the name for the process of remaining in a state of internal stability and balance in the body?

A. Hemostasis
B. Hemolysis
C. Homeostasis
D. Homeopathy

75. What is not required to enter a contact isolation room?

A. Splash-proof face shield

B. Mask

C. Gown

D. Gloves

76. Which OSHA standard includes the need to label a chemical container properly?

A. Standard precautions

B. Hazard communication standard

C. Process safety management of highly hazardous chemicals

D. None of the above

77. What is true about HIV?

A. HIV is more transmittable than Hepatitis

B. Do not shake hands with a patient with HIV

C. HIV is a disease caused by AIDs

D. HIV is a blood-borne pathogen

78. Why are asepsis procedures necessary?

A. Because every patient may carry the risk of disease

B. To ensure patient care areas are sterile

C. To lower the risk of spreading infection

D. None of the above

79. You are drawing a test for multiple tests: CBC, PT, PTT, blood glucose level, and thyroid panel. What is the order of draw?

A. Lavender top, light blue top, gray top, SST top

B. Light blue top, SST, lavender top, gray top

C. SST top, light blue top, lavender top, gray top

D. None of the above

80. When should you not use alcohol swabs for tests?

A. ETOH level

B. Complete blood count
C. Blood cultures
D. A and C

81. How should you choose an appropriate puncture site when performing a heel puncture?

A. Hold the infant's heel and imagine a V-shaped boundary line, the point at the back of the heel. Choose a puncture site outside the V-shaped boundary line on the heel's left side.
B. Hold the infant's heel and imagine a V-shaped boundary line, the point at the back of the heel. Choose a puncture site inside the V-shaped boundary line on the heel's left side.
C. Hold the infant's heel and imagine a V-shaped boundary line, the point at the middle of the foot sole. Choose a puncture site outside the V-shaped boundary line on the heel's left side.
D. Hold the infant's heel and imagine a circle-shaped boundary line. Choose a puncture site on the left side of the heel, outside the boundary line.

82. What is glycolysis?

A. The additive used to preserve glucose in blood
B. Destruction of red blood cells
C. Breaking down glucose for energy
D. Creation of leukocytes in the bone marrow

83. Where is a suitable site for performing an arterial puncture?

A. Antecubital area of both arms
B. The thumb side of the wrist
C. The brachial artery
D. The femoral artery

84. Which of the following cannot be used for blood collection?

A. Syringe draw
B. Intravenous infusion

      C. Vacutainer draws

      D. Butterfly syringe draw

85. A 22-gauge needle can be used for:

      A. Infants

      B. Children

      C. Elderly

      D. B and C

86. If a test is for uric acid, what tube would be used, and to what lab would it be transported?

      A. SST/Chemistry lab

      B. Green/Serology

      C. Lavender/Chemistry lab

      D. Light blue/Serology

87. If a test is for A1C, what tube would be used, and to what lab would it be transported?

      A. SST/Chemistry lab

      B. Green/Serology

      C. Lavender/Chemistry lab

      D. Light blue/Serology

88. What is the purpose of an automatic incision device?

      A. Surgical purposes

      B. Bleeding time punctures

      C. Arterial punctures

      D. Difficult venous puncture

89. What is the most frequently analyzed nonblood body fluid?

      A. Urine

      B. Semen

C. Sweat

D. Sputum

90.   What hormone does the urine pregnancy test examine?

    A. Testosterone
    B. HCG
    C. Estrogen
    D. Progesterone

91.   What is the difference between midstream clean-catch and midstream urine collection methods?

    A. Midstream clean-catch requires special cleaning of the genital area
    B. Midstream only uses catheter
    C. Midstream clean catch requires a plastic bag
    D. Patient

92.   What is the clear fluid surrounding the brain and spinal cord extracted using a lumbar puncture?

    A. Amniotic fluid
    B. Nasopharyngeal secretions
    C. Cerebrospinal fluid
    D. Gastric fluid

93.   What is saliva used for?

    A. To monitor hormone levels
    B. To detect alcohol
    C. To detect drug abuse
    D. All of the above

94.   What test is feces used for?

    A. Clostridium Difficile (C. diff)
    B. Tuberculosis

C. Diabetes

D. Sickle-cell anemia

95. What method is used to collect urine cultures?

A. Midstream urine collection

B. Midstream clean-catch

C. Catheterized

D. Regular void

96. Which blood test requires fasting?

A. Blood glucose

B. Renal function

C. Vitamin B13 test

D. All of the above

97. What is the U.S. amendment passed in 1988 to ensure all clinical laboratories can uphold the high-standard facilities and low risk of test result errors?

A. Patient Bill of Rights

B. Clinical Laboratory Improvement Amendment

C. HIPPA

D. None of the above

98. What are transmission-based precautions?

A. Precautions that target bloodborne pathogens

B. Precautions that aim to reduce opportunities for pathogens to spread

C. Precautions prevent diseases from spreading via droplets, contact, or air

b. All of the above

99. In the order of draw, what comes first, SST or PST?

A. PST goes first

B. SST goes first

C. The order is interchangeable

D. PST and SST are the same

100. What are needle-stick protection devices?

A. Safety control features attached to needle devices

B. Ways to recap needle without risking injury

C. Legally necessary

D. All of the above

Answer Key

Q.	1	2	3	4	5	6	7	8	9	10
A.	B	A	D	A	A	C	C	B	D	D

Q.	11	12	13	14	15	16	17	18	19	20
A.	A	C	B	A	D	A	A	C	C	A

Q.	21	22	23	24	25	26	27	28	29	30
A.	B	D	B	A	A	C	A	D	D	A

Q.	31	32	33	34	35	36	37	38	39	40
A.	B	B	A	D	B	A	C	D	B	B

Q.	41	42	43	44	45	46	47	48	49	50
A.	D	C	A	D	D	B	A	B	D	A

Q.	51	52	53	54	55	56	57	58	59	60
A.	B	D	B	A	C	A	D	D	A	C

Q.	61	62	63	64	65	66	67	68	69	70
A.	B	D	B	C	D	A	C	B	A	A

Q.	71	72	73	74	75	76	77	78	79	80
A.	C	D	A	C	A	B	D	C	B	D

Q.	81	82	83	84	85	86	87	88	89	90
A.	A	C	B	B	D	A	C	C	A	B

Q.	91	92	93	94	95	96	97	98	99	100
A.	A	C	D	A	A	D	B	B	B	D

Answers and Explanations

1. **B** - Failing to mix anticoagulant tubes well enough can result in small clots (micro clots) forming in the specimen.

2. **A** - Tubes without additives should be inverted or mixed.

3. **D** - Platelets activate hemostasis and thrombosis; platelets are sent to an injury site to begin the clotting process.

4. **A** - Routine blood specimens should arrive at the lab within 45 minutes.

5. **A** - The maximum time to separate serum and plasma from blood cells is 2 hours.

6. **C** - Glycolysis is the metabolic process that may occur during handling and transporting, and it must be prevented, as the destruction of glucose can lead to inaccurate lab results.

7. **C** - The arm on the side of a mastectomy should be avoided for venipuncture.

8. **B** - Glycolysis in blood specimens post-draw can lower glucose values on results at 200 mg/L per hour.

9. **D** - SST stands for serum separator tubes.

10. **D** - All of the above; signs of a latex allergy include shortness of breath, a runny nose, hives, and skin redness.

11. **A** - PST stands for plasma separator tube.

12. **C** - Gel barrier tubes do not require manual separation because the gel forms a physical barrier after centrifugation that prevents glycolysis.

13. **B** - A gel barrier can prevent glycolysis for 24 hours.

14. **A** - Blood smears from EDTA specimens must be prepared for the lab within one hour of collection.

15. **D** - Complete blood count specimens remain at room temperature for 24 hours with EDTA.

16. **A** - Arteries and arterioles carry oxygenated blood from the lungs to the heart and body.

17. **A** - Leukocytes (white blood cells) protect the body from infection.

18. **C** - Fibrinolysis is breaking down and removing a clot during hemostasis.

19. **C** - The standard gauge for a multi-sample needle is 21.

20. **A** - Sclerosed veins (hardened, less elastic veins) feel cordlike.

21. **B** - The OGTT (oral glucose tolerance test) diagnoses diabetes.

22. **D** - Failing to use the serum separator properly is one example of post-analytical error.

23. **B** - When veins are winding, they are called tortuous; it can be caused by aging, atherosclerosis, and diabetes.

24. **A** - An NP (nasopharyngeal) culture swab can be used to identify whooping cough.

25. **A** - Do not recap the needle before discarding it, as that is the purpose of resheathing devices.

26. **C** - When a clot activator additive carries over to a blue-topped (coagulation) tube, it leads to a falsely shortened prothrombin time (PT) on test results.

27. **A** - Gray topped tubes are used for lactic acid testing.

28. **D** - Bilirubin, carotene, and RBC folate are light-sensitive specimens.

29. **D** - The royal blue topped tube should be used for a trace elements test.

30. **A** 1-1.5 inch needle should be used for routine venipuncture.

31. **B** - A drug screening blood test requires a chain of custody.

32. **B** - Patients must stop taking medication that may affect test results about 4-24 hours before the blood draw.

33. **A** - The heart's left ventricle delivers oxygenated blood to the aorta.

34. **D** - Glucose has a higher reference range for a capillary puncture.

35. **B** - If a patient has eaten a meal before the blood draw, especially one high in fat, the serum can show up as lipemic.

36. **A** - It is best to assume all patients are infectious and take precautions when it comes to blood-borne pathogens.

37. **C** - An antiglycolytic agent is an additive that prevents glucose from getting broken down in the blood specimen.

38. **D** - A creatinine clearance test requires a 24-hour urine specimen.

39. **B** - A CBC (complete blood count) requires a whole blood specimen.

40. **B** - Specimens in red-topped collection tubes take 30-60 minutes to coagulate naturally.

41. **D** - Failing to provide the proper standard of care, leading to risk or injury, is legally considered negligence.

42. **C** - The Microbiology department is in charge of analyzing Culture & Sensitivity (C&S) tests.

43.   **A** - All healthcare professionals must take the HBV (Hepatitis B virus) vaccine.

44.   **D** - An arterial blood sampling (ABG) specimen must be chilled.

45.   **D** - Light blue tubes should be filled.

46.   **B** - Lymph comes from tissue fluid.

47.   **A** - A pre-analytical error is collecting the specimen at the wrong time.

48.   **B** - A timed specimen is necessary for information about the diurnal variation of cortisol.

49.   **D** - Another word for red blood cells is erythrocytes.

50.   **A** - Tests for ALP, AST, ALT, GTT, and bilirubin are for the liver.

51.   **B** - The pink top EDTA tube is used for a blood type and crossmatch test.

52.   **D** - The lavender tube is drawn last in standard venipuncture.

53.   **B** - Cholesterol and uric acid specimens are least likely to require special handling.

54.   **A** - Performing repeated blood draws to the same site can cause vein inflammation or phlebitis.

55.   **C** - The presence of the HCG hormone indicates a positive pregnancy test.

56.   **A** - The agent is the first link in the chain of infection.

57.   **D** - Drinking too much water does not affect the blood draw.

58.   **D** - Ammonia is not a light-sensitive test; it is temperature sensitive and requires chilling.

59. **A** - The stress hormone cortisol peaks in the morning to provide the initial burst of energy.

60. **C** - A sputum specimen is used to diagnose tuberculosis.

61. **B** - A pink tube contains EDTA.

62. **D** - Glycolysis is faster in newborns because they have a higher metabolism.

63. **B** - Blood flows from arterioles to capillaries to venules.

64. **C** - The light blue topped tube is used for PT and PTT.

65. **D** - The tube's vacuum property sucks blood through into the tube.

66. **A** - It may be necessary to use protective restraints for newborns.

67. **C** - Petechiae indicates clotting problems.

68. **B** - Fibrinogen is found in plasma.

69. **A** - The respiratory system supplies oxygen to the body.

70. **A** - Pulling too quickly on the syringe plunger can lead to hemolysis when transferring blood to a container.

71. **C** - A quality specimen must be non-hemolyzed, non-clotted (if it includes an anticoagulant), and performed at the right patient, with the right tube, and the right test. However, transportation time does not affect the specimen quality.

72. **D** - Active listening and nonverbal communication during interaction with patients mean explaining the process clearly and slowly while maintaining positive body language and eye contact, avoiding interrupting, and allowing the patient to voice concerns or questions.

73. **A** - An incident report is for reporting an incident, like a spillage, injury, exposure, or leak.

74. **C** - Homeostasis means remaining in a state of internal stability in the body.

75. **A** - It is unnecessary to wear a splash-proof face shield to a contact isolation room because contain-based transmission is the main concern.

76. **B** - The Hazard Communication Standard is the OSHA standard that requires properly labeling chemical containers.

77. **D** - HIV is a blood-borne pathogen; AIDS does not cause it, nor is it transmitted by contact (i.e., shaking hands). It is not more transmittable than hepatitis.

78. **C** - Asepsis procedures aim to lower the risk of spreading infection.

79. **B** - Light blue top, SST, lavender top, gray top

80. **D** - Alcohol swabs should not be used for ETOH levels or blood cultures.

81. **A** - Hold the infant's heel and imagine a V-shaped boundary line, the point at the back of the heel. Choose a puncture site outside the V-shaped boundary line on the heel's left side.

82. **C** - Glycolysis is the breakdown of glucose for energy, which can continue to occur in the blood after collection.

83. **B** - The thumb side of the wrist is the best site for an arterial puncture.

84. **B** - Intravenous infusion (IV) should not be used for blood collection.

85. **D** - A 22-gauge needle is suitable for children and the elderly.

86. **A** - A uric acid test would require an SST tube and get processed at the Chemistry lab.

87.　**C** - An A1C test requires a lavender topped tube and is processed at the Chemistry lab.

88.　**C** - The purpose of an automatic incision device (AID) is for bleeding time punctures.

89.　**A** - Urine is the most frequently analyzed nonblood body fluid.

90.　**B** - HCG is the hormone used to indicate pregnancy in a urine test.

91.　**A** - A midstream clean-catch requires special cleaning of the genital area compared to the midstream urine collection.

92.　**C** - Cerebrospinal fluid is a clear fluid that surrounds the brain and spinal cord.

93.　**D** - Salive specimens can monitor hormone levels and detect alcohol or drug abuse.

94.　**A** - A feces specimen can be used for the Clostridium Difficicile test.

95.　**A** - Urine cultures are collected with the midstream urine collection method.

96.　**D** - The blood glucose, renal function, and vitamin B13 tests require fasting.

97.　**B** - The Clinical Laboratory Improvement Amendment (CLIA) was passed to ensure accurate lab results.

98.　**B** - Transmission-based precautions prevent disease transmission via blood and other bodily fluids in healthcare.

99.　**B** - SST should always come first in the order of draw, then PST.

100.　**D** - Needle-stick protection devices are all of the above; legally necessary safety control features attached to needle devices that allow phlebotomists to recap needles without risking injury.

Conclusion

The NHA Phlebotomy Exam Study Guide aims to help you be as ready as possible for the Exam.

Make sure to go through the information in each section repeatedly to familiarize yourself with the most crucial aspects of the exam. If you read through this, memorize critical information, and use the practice tests to gain mastery over the content, you can be assured you will be well-equipped to succeed in acing the exam and becoming a phlebotomist.

Finally, please leave a review so other students can also master their exams.

References

n.d. Appropriate Maximum Phlebotomy Volumes. Accessed June 10, 2022. https://www.childrensmn.org/departments/lab/pdf/phleb2.pdf.

n.d. Appropriate Maximum Phlebotomy Volumes. Accessed June 16, 2022. https://www.childrensmn.org/departments/lab/pdf/phleb2.pdf.

n.d. Specimen Labeling and Handling. Accessed June 16, 2022. https://apps.trihealth.com/trihealthlab/SpecimenLabelHandle.pdf.

n.d. Centrifuging Serum and Plasma. Accessed June 16, 2022. https://www.eehealth.org/-/media/files/edward-elmhurst/services/lab/centrifuge-operation-062016.pdf.

Aboamer, Ahmed. n.d. "phlebotomy related vascular anatomy." SlideShare. Accessed June 9, 2022. https://www.slideshare.net/AhmedAboamer/phlebotomy-related-vascular-anatomy.

"ABO blood group system | Definition, Blood Type, & ABO Antigens." n.d. Encyclopedia Britannica. Accessed June 16, 2022. https://www.britannica.com/science/ABO-blood-group-system.

"About Our Standards." n.d. The Joint Commission. Accessed June 10, 2022. https://www.jointcommission.org/standards/about-our-standards/.

Access Health Care Physicians. 2019. "Palpating a Vein." YouTube. https://www.youtube.com/watch?v=L3HC-NbkRHE.

Ahmad, Farhan. 2022. "complications during blood collection and treatment." Labpedia.net. https://labpedia.net/complications-during-blood-collection-and-treatment/.

"Aliquoting a Specimen CHI Health Lab Form." n.d. CHI Health. Accessed June 16, 2022. https://www.chihealth.com/content/dam/chi-health/website/documents/lab/collection-and-transport/preparation/aliquoting-specimens.pdf.

"Aliquoting Demonstration & How To Video." 2011. YouTube. https://www.youtube.com/watch?v=mnS0pAdNd3k.

Allied Health Program. 2020. "Learning Phlebotomy Equipment | Arizona College." Arizona College of Nursing. https://www.arizonacollege.edu/blog/phlebotomy-equipment/.

AlliedHealthToolsLLC. 2021. "Introduction to Laboratory Requisition Forms." YouTube. https://www.youtube.com/watch?v=RL2nlP28500.

"Aseptic technique for blood collection and its significance in Microbiology." 2019. YouTube. https://www.youtube.com/watch?v=UeNTUtkuNM4.

Beaumont Laboratory. n.d. "Blood Collection via Venipuncture." Geriatric Phlebotomy Tips. Accessed June 16, 2022. https://www.beaumontlaboratory.com/docs/default-source/specimen-collections-manual/blood/p7855k25_24055_061521_geriatric_phlebotomy_tips.p.

Beaumont Laboratory. n.d. "Geriatric Phlebotomy Tips." Accessed June 10, 2022. https://www.beaumontlaboratory.com/docs/default-source/specimen-collections-manual/blood/p7855k25_24055_061521_geriatric_phlebotomy_tips.p.

"Best practices in phlebotomy - WHO Guidelines on Drawing Blood." n.d. NCBI. Accessed June 10, 2022. https://www.ncbi.nlm.nih.gov/books/NBK138665/.

"Best practices in phlebotomy - WHO Guidelines on Drawing Blood." n.d. NCBI. Accessed June 16, 2022. https://www.ncbi.nlm.nih.gov/books/NBK138665/.

"Best practices in phlebotomy - WHO Guidelines on Drawing Blood." n.d. NCBI. Accessed June 16, 2022. https://www.ncbi.nlm.nih.gov/books/NBK138665/.

"Biohazardous and Medical Waste Overview." 2020. UCSD Blink. https://blink.ucsd.edu/safety/research-lab/hazardous-waste/disposal-guidance/medical/index.html.

"Blood Alcohol Collection - Idaho Falls." n.d. Express Lab. Accessed June 16, 2022. https://www.expresslabidaho.com/collection-tips/blood-alcohol-collection/.

"Bloodborne Pathogen Cleanup: Important Facts to Know." n.d. Aftermath Services. Accessed June 10, 2022. https://www.aftermath.com/content/bloodborne-pathogen-cleanup/.

"Blood Collection Procedure: Capillary » Pathology Laboratories » College of Medicine » University of Florida." n.d. UF Health Pathology Laboratories. Accessed June 16, 2022. https://pathlabs.ufl.edu/client-services/specimen-shipping/blood-collection-procedure-capillary/.

"Blood Collection: Special Considerations." 2017. YouTube. https://www.youtube.com/watch?v=Hr0jLuOhLAs.

"Blood Collection Systems: Straight Needle, Syringe and Butterfly." 2017. YouTube. https://www.youtube.com/watch?v=Y4Apdlqols8.

"Blood Culture Collection Procedure." 2022. Pathology-Lab Users Guide. https://lug.hfhs.org/bloodCult.htm.

"Blood groups." n.d. NHS. Accessed June 16, 2022. https://www.nhs.uk/conditions/blood-groups/.

"Blood Smear." 2021. MedlinePlus. https://medlineplus.gov/lab-tests/blood-smear/.

"Blood Specimens: Chemistry and Hematology." n.d. Labcorp.

Accessed June 16, 2022. https://www.labcorp.com/resource/blood-specimens-chemistry-and-hematology.

"Blood Tube Labeling Information." n.d. LabCE. Accessed June 9, 2022. https://www.labce.com/spg263740_blood_tube_labeling_information.

"Blood Tube Labeling Information." n.d. Laboratory Continuing Education. Accessed June 16, 2022. https://www.labce.com/spg263740_blood_tube_labeling_information.

Bour, Evita. 2012. "Phlebotomy equipment & accessories for phlebotomists." Phlebotomy Training Group. https://phlebotomytraininggroup.com/phlebotomy-equipment/.

Bouza, Emilio, Dolores Sousa, Marta Rodriguez-Créixems, Juan G. Lechuz, and Patricia Muñoz. n.d. "Is the Volume of Blood Cultured Still a Significant Factor in the Diagnosis of Bloodstream Infections?" NCBI. Accessed June 16, 2022. https://www.ncbi.nlm.nih.gov/pmc/articles/PMC2045273/.

Buowari, Omiepirisa Y. 2013. Complications of venepuncture. https://file.scirp.org/pdf/ABB_2013013114170934.pdf.

Calfee, David P., and Barry M. Farr. 2002. "Comparison of Four Antiseptic Preparations for Skin in the Prevention of Contamination of Percutaneously Drawn Blood Cultures: a Randomized Trial." NCBI. https://www.ncbi.nlm.nih.gov/pmc/articles/PMC130950/.

"Capillary sampling - WHO Guidelines on Drawing Blood." n.d. NCBI. Accessed June 16, 2022. https://www.ncbi.nlm.nih.gov/books/NBK138654/.

"Centrifugation and Aliquoting of Blood Serum and Plasma." 2017. YouTube. https://www.youtube.com/watch?v=XAhBzUosvsU.

"Centrifuge Operation for Phlebotomy." 2020. YouTube. https://www.youtube.com/watch?v=1PETST8GJak.

"Chain of Custody Testing." n.d. Mayo Clinic Laboratories. Accessed June

16, 2022. https://www.mayocliniclabs.com/test-catalog/drug-book/chain-of-custody-testing.

"Cleansing the Venipuncture Site." n.d. Laboratory Continuing Education. Accessed June 16, 2022. https://www.labce.com/spg263744_cleansing_the_venipuncture_site.

Close, Anthony. 2018. "Factors That Can Affect The Laboratory Tests." Lab Me. https://www.labme.ai/factors-that-can-affect-the-laboratory-tests/.

"Common Gauges of Needles Used for Venipuncture." n.d. PhlebotomyU. Accessed June 10, 2022. https://phlebotomyu.com/common-gauges-of-needles-used-for-venipuncture/.

"Common Gauges of Needles Used for Venipuncture." n.d. PhlebotomyU. Accessed June 16, 2022. https://phlebotomyu.com/common-gauges-of-needles-used-for-venipuncture/.

"Complying with Laboratory Services Documentation Requirements." 2020. CMS. https://www.cms.gov/Outreach-and-Education/Medicare-Learning-Network-MLN/MLNProducts/Downloads/LabServices-ICN909221-Text-Only.pdf.

"Complying with Laboratory Services Documentation Requirements." n.d. CMS. Accessed June 16, 2022. https://www.cms.gov/Outreach-and-Education/Medicare-Learning-Network-MLN/MLNProducts/Downloads/LabServices-ICN909221-Text-Only.pdf.

"Critical Values." n.d. Labcorp. Accessed June 16, 2022. https://www.labcorp.com/resource/critical-values.

"Critical Values | Services for Health Care Professionals | Pathology and Lab Services." n.d. Main Line Health. Accessed June 16, 2022. https://www.mainlinehealth.org/specialties/pathology/services-for-health-care-professionals/critical-values.

Di Lorenzo, Marjorie S., and Susan K. Strasinger. 2019. The Phlebotomy Textbook. February: F.A. Davis Company.

"Disposal methods for blood collection tubes. | Occupational Safety and Health Administration." n.d. OSHA. Accessed June 16, 2022. https://www.osha.gov/laws-regs/standardinterpretations/2000-03-13.

"Effective Communication." n.d. LabCE. Accessed June 9, 2022. https://www.labce.com/spg549512_effective_communication.aspx.

"Effect of Pre-Analytical Errors on Quality of Laboratory Medicine at a Neuropsychiatry Institute in North India." n.d. NCBI. Accessed June 16, 2022. https://www.ncbi.nlm.nih.gov/pmc/articles/PMC3068767/.

Ernst, Dennis. 2018. "Standards Update: Circular cleansing." Center for Phlebotomy Education. https://www.phlebotomy.com/phlebotomyblog/standards-up-date-circular-cleansing.html.

Ernst, Dennis. 2020. "What Every Phlebotomist Must Know About Drawing Coags." Center for Phlebotomy Education. https://www.phlebotomy.com/phlebotomyblog/what-every-phlebotomist-must-know-about-drawing-coags.html.

Ernst, Dennis. 2020. "What Every Phlebotomist Must Know About Drawing Coags." Center for Phlebotomy Education. https://www.phlebotomy.com/phlebotomyblog/what-every-phlebotomist-must-know-about-drawing-coags.html.

Ernst, Dennis. 2021. "How to Manage Patients Who Pass Out." Center for Phlebotomy Education. https://www.phlebotomy.com/phlebotomyblog/safety/managing-patients-who-lose-consciousness.html.

"Ethical Issues in Phlebotomy." 2019. Insights. https://news.mayocliniclabs.com/2019/12/18/ethical-issues-in-phlebotomy/.

"Exposure Control Plan for Bloodborne Pathogens." 2017. Infection Control Manual. https://ehs.unc.edu/wp-content/uploads/sites/229/2015/08/bbpexposurecontrol.pdf.

"Factors Affecting Blood Test Results PX-SC250." n.d. Alberta Health Services.

Accessed June 10, 2022. https://www.albertahealthservices.ca/assets/wf/lab/if-lab-tc-cal-factors-affecting-blood-test-results-px-sc250.pdf.

"Factors Affecting Blood Test Results PX-SC250." n.d. Alberta Health Services. Accessed June 15, 2022. https://www.albertahealthservices.ca/assets/wf/lab/if-lab-tc-cal-factors-affecting-blood-test-results-px-sc250.pdf.

"Factors That Can Affect The Laboratory Tests." 2018. Lab Me. https://www.labme.ai/factors-that-can-affect-the-laboratory-tests/.

"Fasting specimen | definition of fasting specimen by Medical dictionary." n.d. Medical Dictionary. Accessed June 16, 2022. https://medical-dictionary.thefreedictionary.com/fasting+specimen.

Gaines, Kathleen. 2022. "How To Draw Blood: A Step-By-Step Guide." Nurse.org. https://nurse.org/articles/how-nurses-professionally-draw-blood/.

Garcia, Matt. n.d. "How to Troubleshoot a Difficult Venipuncture: 14 Steps." wikiHow. Accessed June 16, 2022. https://www.wikihow.com/Troubleshoot-a-Difficult-Venipuncture.

George, Caitlin. 2015. "Why must unused blood tubes be discarded when they expire (phlebotomy)?" Quora. https://www.quora.com/Why-must-unused-blood-tubes-be-discarded-when-they-expire-phlebotomy.

"Geriatric Patients." n.d. LabCE. Accessed June 16, 2022. https://www.labce.com/spg549532_geriatric_patients.aspx.

Glasgow, Nancy. 2021. "Best practices in capillary blood collection." Medical Laboratory Observer. https://www.mlo-online.com/diagnostics/specimen-collection/article/21206382/best-practices-in-capillary-blood-collection.

Gundersen Health System Laboratories. n.d. "Tube Fill Requirements." Specimen Collection. Accessed June 10, 2022. https://www.gundersenhealth.org/app/files/public/c5af4b8d-3be7-4c57-a555-6fb9b1af9b38/Laboratory-Tube-fill-requirements.pdf.

Gundersen Health System Laboratories. n.d. "Tube Fill Requirements and Common Causes of Specimen Rejection Guide for Nurses." Specimen Collection. Accessed June 16, 2022. https://www.gundersenhealth.org/app/files/public/c5af4b8d-3be7-4c57-a555-6fb9b1af9b38/Laboratory-Tube-fill-requirements.pdf.

"Handling, Processing, Storing and Delivering Specimens." 2017. YouTube. https://www.youtube.com/watch?v=Jm7I-kqRqH4.

Healthwise. 2020. "Skin and Wound Cultures." University of Michigan Health. https://www.uofmhealth.org/health-library/hw5656.

"Hematology Glossary." n.d. American Society of Hematology. Accessed June 10, 2022. https://www.hematology.org/education/patients/blood-basics.

"Hemostasis: Stages and How the Process Stops Blood Flow." 2021. Cleveland Clinic. https://my.clevelandclinic.org/health/symptoms/21999-hemostasis.

"HIPAA PRIVACY REGULATIONS Objectives • Develop a basic understanding of the HIPAA Privacy Regulations • Understand the impac." n.d. Self Regional Healthcare. Accessed June 10, 2022. https://www.selfregional.org/wp-content/uploads/2015/12/HIPAA-Privacy-Student-Passport.pdf.

"HIPAA PRIVACY REGULATIONS Objectives • Develop a basic understanding of the HIPAA Privacy Regulations • Understand the impac." n.d. Self Regional Healthcare. Accessed June 10, 2022. https://www.selfregional.org/wp-content/uploads/2015/12/HIPAA-Privacy-Student-Passport.pdf.

"How to Anchor the Vein." n.d. PhlebotomyU. Accessed June 16, 2022. https://phlebotomyu.com/how-to-anchor-the-vein/.

"How to apply a venous tourniquet correctly (a venipuncture training video)." 2013. YouTube. https://www.youtube.com/watch?v=Dx-yc84QbMs.

"How to Apply & Tie a Tourniquet When Drawing Blood or Starting an IV." 2014. YouTube. https://www.youtube.com/watch?v=jJL8uCVgfVM.

"How to do a Successful Blood Draw." 2013. Arizona College of Nursing. https://www.arizonacollege.edu/blog/needle-positioning-the-key-to-a-successful-blood-draw/.

"HR5178 - 106th Congress (1999-2000): Needlestick Safety and Prevention Act | Congress.gov | Library of Congress." n.d. Congress.gov. Accessed June 16, 2022. https://www.congress.gov/bill/106th-congress/house-bill/5178.

"Infection Control and Prevention - Transmission-based precautions | Wisconsin Department of Health Services." 2020. Wisconsin Department of Health Services. https://www.dhs.wisconsin.gov/ic/transmission.htm.

"Infection Control and Prevention - Transmission-based precautions | Wisconsin Department of Health Services." 2020. Wisconsin Department of Health Services. https://www.dhs.wisconsin.gov/ic/transmission.htm.

"Introduction to Specimen Collection." n.d. Labcorp. Accessed June 16, 2022. https://www.labcorp.com/resource/introduction-to-specimen-collection.

"Introduction to the Cardiovascular System." n.d. SEER Training. Accessed June 16, 2022. https://training.seer.cancer.gov/anatomy/cardiovascular/.

"Iv Gauge Needles | What are the Differences Between 18, 20, 22, Gauge Needles." 2014. YouTube. https://www.youtube.com/watch?v=abIrfrnaPfg.

Jahreis, Larissa. 2020. What is the chain of custody in phlebotomy? https://find-anyanswer.com/what-is-the-chain-of-custody-in-phlebotomy.

Kaushik, Nitin. 2014. "Pre-analytical errors: their impact and how to minimize them." Medical Laboratory Observer. https://www.mlo-online.com/home/article/13006606/preanalytical-errors-their-impact-and-how-to-minimize-them.

Kohli, Payal. 2021. "Cardiovascular system: Function, organs, diseases, and more." Medical News Today. https://www.medicalnewstoday.com/articles/cardiovascular-system.

Kozey, Emanuel. n.d. "Which phlebotomy tubes need to be centrifuged?" Movie Cultists. Accessed June 16, 2022. https://moviecultists.com/which-phlebotomy-tubes-need-to-be-centrifuged.

Krause, Lydia. n.d. "Blood Smear: Purpose, Procedure, and Results." Healthline. Accessed June 16, 2022. https://www.healthline.com/health/blood-smear.

Kurec, Anthony. 2016. "Proper patient preparation, specimen collection, and sample handling are critical to quality care." Medical Laboratory Observer. https://www.mlo-online.com/diagnostics/specimen-collection/article/13008896/proper-patient-preparation-specimen-collection-and-sample-handling-are-critical-to-quality-care.

"Lab Forms and Test Requisition Forms FAQ - Common Answers to Questions." n.d. Unisource Printing. Accessed June 10, 2022. https://unisourceprinting.com/test-requisition-form-faq/.

"Lab Forms and Test Requisition Forms FAQ - Common Answers to Questions." n.d. Unisource Printing. Accessed June 16, 2022. https://unisourceprinting.com/test-requisition-form-faq/.

"Laboratories - Overview | Occupational Safety and Health Administration." n.d. OSHA. Accessed June 10, 2022. https://www.osha.gov/laboratories.

"Laboratory Test Requisition (Outreach) » Laboratory Alliance of Central New York, LLC." n.d. Laboratory Alliance. Accessed June 10, 2022. https://www.laboratoryalliance.com/healthcare-providers/laboratory-services/specimen-collection-documents/laboratory-requisition/.

"Laboratory Test Requisition (Outreach) » Laboratory Alliance of Central New York, LLC." n.d. Laboratory Alliance. Accessed June 16, 2022. https://www.laboratoryalliance.com/healthcare-providers/laboratory-services/specimen-collection-documents/laboratory-requisition/.

"Learning Phlebotomy Equipment | Arizona College." 2020. Arizona College of Nursing. https://www.arizonacollege.edu/blog/phlebotomy-equipment/.

"Legal Issues in Phlebotomy." n.d. PhlebotomyU. Accessed June 10, 2022. https://phlebotomyu.com/legal-issues-in-phlebotomy/.

"Master's Guide to Venipuncture: Pro Tips for Performing Venipuncture." 2020. Unitek College. https://www.unitekcollege.edu/blog/stick-like-a-pro-tips-for-mastering-the-art-of-venipuncture/.

"Maximum Blood Draw on Pediatric Patients | Novant Health New Hanover Regional Medical Center | Wilmington, NC." n.d. New Hanover Regional Medical Center. Accessed June 16, 2022. https://www.nhrmc.org/healthcare-professionals/laboratory/specimen-collection/maximum-blood-draw-pediatric-patients.

"Maximum Blood Draw on Pediatric Patients | Novant Health New Hanover Regional Medical Center | Wilmington, NC." n.d. New Hanover Regional Medical Center. Accessed June 16, 2022. https://www.nhrmc.org/healthcare-professionals/laboratory/specimen-collection/maximum-blood-draw-pediatric-patients.

MCL Education. 2019. "Ethical Issues in Phlebotomy." Insights. https://news.mayocliniclabs.com/2019/12/18/ethical-issues-in-phlebotomy/.

"Misidentified Patients and Samples:." n.d. Center for Phlebotomy Education. Accessed June 10, 2022. https://www.phlebotomy.com/misidentified-patients-and-samples.html.

"Misidentified Patients and Samples:." n.d. Center for Phlebotomy Education. Accessed June 15, 2022. https://www.phlebotomy.com/misidentified-patients-and-samples.html.

"Molecular (PCR) Testing." n.d. Clinical Pathology Laboratories. Accessed June 16, 2022. https://www.cpllabs.com/covid-19/healthcare-providers/molecular-pcr-testing/.

"NAPTP Code of Ethics - NAPTP." n.d. naptp. Accessed June 9, 2022. https://naptp.com/naptp-code-of-ethics/.

"NAPTP Code of Ethics - NAPTP." n.d. National Association of Phlebotomy

Technician Professionals. Accessed June 16, 2022. https://naptp.com/naptp-code-of-ethics/.

"NAPTP Code of Ethics - NAPTP." n.d. National Association of Phlebotomy Technician Professionals. Accessed June 16, 2022. https://naptp.com/naptp-code-of-ethics/.

"NPPN." n.d. NPPN. Accessed June 10, 2022. https://nppn.info/index.php/pages/hipaa_privacy_policy.

Occupational Safety and Health Administration. n.d. "Medical and First Aid." OSHA. Accessed June 10, 2022. https://www.osha.gov/medical-first-aid/recognition.

Occupational Safety & Health Administration. n.d. "Worker protections against occupational exposure to infectious diseases." Bloodborne Pathogens. Accessed June 10, 2022. https://www.osha.gov/bloodborne-pathogens/worker-protections.

O'Connor, Krista. 2018. "Phlebotomy Ethics." Career Trend. https://careertrend.com/facts-6849424-phlebotomy-ethics.html.

Ohnishi, Hiroaki. 2005. "[Side effects of phlebotomy: pathophysiology, diagnosis, treatment and prophylaxis]." PubMed. https://pubmed.ncbi.nlm.nih.gov/16296336/.

"Order of Blood Draw Tubes and Additives." 2019. Clinical and Laboratory Standards Institute (CLSI). https://clsi.org/about/blog/order-of-blood-draw-tubes-and-additives/.

"Order of Blood Draw Tubes and Additives." 2019. Clinical and Laboratory Standards Institute (CLSI). https://clsi.org/about/blog/order-of-blood-draw-tubes-and-additives/.

"The Order of Draw:." n.d. Center for Phlebotomy Education. Accessed June 10, 2022. https://www.phlebotomy.com/the-order-of-draw.html.

"The Order of Draw:." n.d. Center for Phlebotomy Education. Accessed June 16, 2022. https://www.phlebotomy.com/the-order-of-draw.html.

Parker, Christopher. 2021. "Evacuated Blood Collection Tube Guide | McLendon Clinical Laboratories." UNC Medical Center. https://www.uncmedicalcenter. org/mclendon-clinical-laboratories/test-specifications/tube-guide/.

Parker, Christopher. 2021. "Evacuated Blood Collection Tube Guide | McLendon Clinical Laboratories." UNC Medical Center. https://www.uncmedicalcenter. org/mclendon-clinical-laboratories/test-specifications/tube-guide/.

Parker, Christopher. 2021. "Evacuated Blood Collection Tube Guide | McLendon Clinical Laboratories." UNC Medical Center. https://www.uncmedicalcenter. org/mclendon-clinical-laboratories/test-specifications/tube-guide/.

"Patient Position." n.d. LabCE. Accessed June 10, 2022. https://www.labce.com/ spg803243_patient_position.aspx.

"PEDIATRIC BLOOD VOLUME DRAW GUIDANCE." n.d. Children's & Women's Health Centre of British Columbia. Accessed June 16, 2022. http:// www.phsa.ca/research/Documents/pediatric-blood-draw-guidance.pdf.

"Phlebotomist: How to Anchor a Vein and Insert a Needle." 2011. Allied Health World. https://www.alliedhealthworld.com/blog/phlebotomist-how-to-an-chor-a-vein-and-insert-a-needle.html.

"Phlebotomy: 5 Tips on Finding Difficult Veins | CPT1 Course." n.d. PhlebotomyU. Accessed June 16, 2022. https://phlebotomyu.com/ phlebotomy-finding-difficult-veins/.

"Phlebotomy Chapter 2 Flashcards." n.d. Quizlet. Accessed June 9, 2022. https:// quizlet.com/215516767/phlebotomy-chapter-2-flash-cards/.

"Phlebotomy Equipment." 2020. YouTube. https://www.youtube.com/ watch?v=7YWdxgtXGwI.

"Phlebotomy for Too Much Iron – Health Information Library." n.d. PeaceHealth.

Accessed June 16, 2022. https://www.peacehealth.org/medical-topics/id/uh1552.

"Phlebotomy | issues and complications– Gafacom." 2020. Gafacom. https://gafacom.website/phlebotomy-issues-and-complications-management/.

"Phlebotomy Medical Terminology (And Practice Test)." n.d. Phlebotomy Coach. Accessed June 10, 2022. https://phlebotomycoach.com/resources/phlebotomy-terminology.

"Phlebotomy Medical Terminology (And Practice Test)." n.d. Phlebotomy Coach. Accessed June 16, 2022. https://phlebotomycoach.com/resources/phlebotomy-terminology.

"Phlebotomy Needle Device Safety Features." n.d. PhlebotomyU. Accessed June 16, 2022. https://phlebotomyu.com/phlebotomy-needle-device-safety-features/.

"phlebotomy related vascular anatomy." n.d. SlideShare. Accessed June 16, 2022. https://www.slideshare.net/AhmedAboamer/phlebotomy-related-vascular-anatomy.

"Phlebotomy Site Selection." n.d. Infusion Therapy Institute. Accessed June 10, 2022. https://www.infusioninstitute.com/courses/phlebotomy-and-blood-specimen-collection/lessons/phlebotomy-site-selection/.

"Phlebotomy Site Selection." n.d. Infusion Therapy Institute. Accessed June 16, 2022. https://www.infusioninstitute.com/courses/phlebotomy-and-blood-specimen-collection/lessons/phlebotomy-site-selection/.

Phlebotomy Solutions. 2016. "Phlebotomy: The Order of Draw." YouTube. https://www.youtube.com/watch?v=RlQWhhVwzaI.

Phlebotomy Solutions. 2017. "Blood Collection Systems: Straight Needle, Syringe and Butterfly." YouTube. https://www.youtube.com/watch?v=Y4Apdlqols8.

"Phlebotomy Technician - Explore Health Care Careers - Mayo Clinic College of

Medicine & Science." n.d. Mayo Clinic College of Medicine. Accessed June 10, 2022. https://college.mayo.edu/academics/explore-health-care-careers/careers-a-z/phlebotomy-technician/.

"Phlebotomy Technician - Explore Health Care Careers - Mayo Clinic College of Medicine & Science." n.d. Mayo Clinic College of Medicine. Accessed June 16, 2022. https://college.mayo.edu/academics/explore-health-care-careers/careers-a-z/phlebotomy-technician/.

"Phlebotomy: The Order of Draw." 2016. YouTube. https://www.youtube.com/watch?v=RlQWhhVwzaI.

"Phlebotomy: The Order of Draw." 2016. YouTube. https://www.youtube.com/watch?v=RlQWhhVwzaI.

"Phlebotomy Top Gun: Safe Handling of Laboratory Specimens During the COVID-19 Pandemic - Insights." 2022. Insights. https://news.mayocliniclabs.com/2022/02/28/%ef%bf%bcphlebotomy-top-gun-safe-handling-of-laboratory-specimens-during-the-covid-19-pandemic/.

"Phlebotomy: Tourniquet Application." 2018. YouTube. https://www.youtube.com/watch?v=aXVdAJNfkGM.

Phlebotomy Training Group. 2012. "Introduction to venipuncture for phlebotomy professionals." Phlebotomy Training Group. https://phlebotomytraininggroup.com/venipuncture/.

Phlebotomy Training Group. 2013. "Phlebotomy Safety Regulations and Procedures." Phlebotomy Training Group. https://phlebotomytraininggroup.com/phlebotomy-safety-regulations-procedures/.

"Phlebotomy tutorial for medical education." n.d. WebPath. Accessed June 10, 2022. https://webpath.med.utah.edu/TUTORIAL/PHLEB/PHLEB.html#:~:tex.

"Phlebotomy tutorial for medical education." n.d. WebPath. Accessed June 16, 2022. https://webpath.med.utah.edu/TUTORIAL/PHLEB/PHLEB.html#:~:tex.

"Positioning Pediatric Patients." 2015. YouTube. https://www.youtube.com/watch?v=pCsLzW_hoOo.

"Positioning Pediatric Patients." 2015. YouTube. https://www.youtube.com/watch?v=pCsLzW_hoOo.

"Post-analytical laboratory work: national recommendations from the Working Group for Post-analytics on behalf of the Croatian Society of Medical Biochemistry and Laboratory Medicine." 2019. NCBI. https://www.ncbi.nlm.nih.gov/pmc/articles/PMC6559616/.

"Procedures/Risks: blood draws, IV lines, vitals_template." n.d. OSU CCTS. Accessed June 16, 2022. https://ccts.osu.edu/sites/default/files/inline-files/Procedures_Risks-Blood_draws-IVs-vitals-etc.pdf.

Ranjitkar, Pratistha. 2015. "Phlebotomy and Tube Type Selection | AACC. org." American Association for Clinical Chemistry. https://www.aacc.org/science-and-research/clinical-chemistry-trainee-council/trainee-council-in-english/pearls-of-laboratory-medicine/2015/phlebotomy-and-tube-type-selection.

Ranjitkar, Pratistha. 2015. "Phlebotomy and Tube Type Selection | AACC. org." American Association for Clinical Chemistry. https://www.aacc.org/science-and-research/clinical-chemistry-trainee-council/trainee-council-in-english/pearls-of-laboratory-medicine/2015/phlebotomy-and-tube-type-selection.

"RECOMMENDATIONS FOR BLOOD CULTURE COLLECTION." n.d. bioMérieux Clinical Diagnostics. Accessed June 16, 2022. https://www.biomerieux-diagnostics.com/sites/clinic/files/9313564-010-gb-d_-_blood_culture_flyer_final_ok.pdf.

"Role of Phlebotomist." 2021. Work - Chron.com. https://work.chron.com/role-phlebotomist-15696.html.

"Role of Phlebotomist." n.d. Work - Chron.com. Accessed June 16, 2022. https://work.chron.com/role-phlebotomist-15696.html.

Sabatino, Charles. 2021. "Informed Consent - Special Subjects." Merck Manuals. https://www.merckmanuals.com/professional/special-subjects/ medicolegal-issues/informed-consent.

Safe Injection Global Network. 2010. "WHO guidelines on drawing blood : best practices in phlebotomy." CDC stacks. https://stacks.cdc.gov/view/cdc/41566.

Salvagno, Gian L., Elisa Danese, Gabriel Lima-Oliveira, Gian C. Guidi, and Giuseppe Lippi. 2013. "Avoidance to wipe alcohol before venipuncture is not a source of spurious hemolysis." NCBI. https://www.ncbi.nlm.nih.gov/pmc/ articles/PMC3900069/.

"Selecting The Venipuncture Site." n.d. StudyLib. Accessed June 10, 2022. https:// studylib.net/doc/8084410/selecting-the-venipuncture-site.

"Selecting The Venipuncture Site." n.d. StudyLib. Accessed June 16, 2022. https:// studylib.net/doc/8084410/selecting-the-venipuncture-site.

Seth, Vivek. 2017. "Home Healthcare Privacy Informed Consent: Express or Implied Consent?" Colleaga. https://www.colleaga.org/article/ informed-consent-express-or-implied-consent.

"Special Populations and Blood Draws." 2016. YouTube. https://www.youtube. com/watch?v=L3X2mcoygDA.

"SPECIMEN COLLECTION PROCEDURE VENIPUNCTURE AND CENTRIFUGATION." 2018. CDL Laboratories. https://www.cdllaborato- ries.com/download/en/procedures/LA-75-WI-020E.pdf.

"Specimen Collection & Processing Procedures." n.d. UCHealth. Accessed June 16, 2022. https://www.uchealth.org/professionals/uch-clinical-laboratory/ specimen-collecting-handling-guide/specimen-collection-procedures/.

"Specimen Labeling Requirements | Department of Pathology | School of Medicine." n.d. University of California, Irvine. Accessed June 16, 2022. https://www.pa- thology.uci.edu/services/specimen-labeling-requirements.asp.

"Specimen Requirements/Containers." n.d. Department of Pathology & Laboratory Medicine. Accessed June 10, 2022. https://www.pathology.uci.edu//services/specimen-containers.asp.

"Specimen Requirements/Containers." n.d. Department of Pathology & Laboratory Medicine. Accessed June 16, 2022. https://www.pathology.uci.edu//services/specimen-containers.asp.

Srikanth, Kishan K., and Saran Lotfollahzadeh. 2022. "Phlebotomy - StatPearls." NCBI. https://www.ncbi.nlm.nih.gov/books/NBK574569/.

"Standard Precautions for All Patient Care | Basics | Infection Control | CDC." n.d. Centers for Disease Control and Prevention. Accessed June 10, 2022. https://www.cdc.gov/infectioncontrol/basics/standard-precautions.html.

SUNSOARS. 2013. "Phlebotomy: Dermal Capillary Punctures | Blood Collection (Rx-TN)." YouTube. https://www.youtube.com/watch?v=ibU5PYOF2qg.

"10 Preparation AND Handling of Nonblood Specimens - MEDICAL LABORATORY SCIENCE PROGRAM PRINCIPLES OF." n.d. StuDocu. Accessed June 10, 2022. https://www.studocu.com/ph/document/san-pedro-college/medical-laboratory-science/10-preparation-and-handling-of-nonblood-specimens/8653087.

"The Zen of Phlebotomy: How To Label a Blood Sample." 2020. YouTube. https://www.youtube.com/watch?v=SHSfIT2Rvyw."Throat swab culture." 2020. MedlinePlus. https://medlineplus.gov/ency/article/003746.htm.

"Tourniquets, Alcohol, and Gauze." n.d. Laboratory Continuing Education. Accessed June 16, 2022. https://www.labce.com/spg263743_tourniquets_alcohol_and_gauze.

Usman Waheed, BS (MLT), MPhil Biochem, Muhammad Asim Ansari, BS (MLT), MSc Biochem, Hasan Abbas Zaheer, MBBS, Phlebotomy as the Backbone of the Laboratory, Laboratory Medicine, Volume 44, Issue 1, February 2013, Pages e69–e71, https://doi.org/10.1309/LMC7WIA8Z7VVBSTO

"Venipuncture class - Part 1 - FHCAOrlando.com." 2019. FHCA Orlando. https://fhcaorlando.com/venipuncture-class-part-1/.

"Venipuncture class - Part 1 - FHCAOrlando.com." 2019. FHCA Orlando. https://fhcaorlando.com/venipuncture-class-part-1/.

"Venipuncture Procedures." n.d. Blood Collection Procedures. Accessed June 10, 2022. https://downloads.lww.com/wolterskluwer_vitalstream_com/sample-content/9781451194524_McCall/samples/Chapter08.pdf.

"Venous Insufficiency: Ambulatory Phlebectomy - PMC." n.d. NCBI. Accessed June 16, 2022. https://www.ncbi.nlm.nih.gov/pmc/articles/PMC3036274/.

"The Vital Role of Phlebotomists in Medical Care." 2016. South Florida Health Care Institute. https://www.sflhealthcareinstitute.com/the-vital-role-of-phlebotomists-in-medical-care.

"Waived Tests | CDC." n.d. Centers for Disease Control and Prevention. Accessed June 10, 2022. https://www.cdc.gov/labquality/waived-tests.html.

Wegerbauer, Beth. n.d. "How to Avoid Preanalytical Testing Errors: A Virtual Roundtable Discussion." Acutecaretesting.org. Accessed June 16, 2022. https://acutecaretesting.org/en/articles/how-to-avoid-preanalytical-testing-errors-a-virtual-roundtable-discussion.

Wegerbauer, Beth. n.d. "How to Avoid Preanalytical Testing Errors: A Virtual Roundtable Discussion." Acutecaretesting.org. Accessed June 16, 2022. https://acutecaretesting.org/en/articles/how-to-avoid-preanalytical-testing-errors-a-virtual-roundtable-discussion.

"What is CPR." n.d. American Heart Association CPR. Accessed June 10, 2022. https://cpr.heart.org/en/resources/what-is-cpr.

"What Is the Difference Between Express and Implied Consent?" 2020. Stephens Law Firm, PLLC. https://www.stephenslaw.com/blog/what-is-the-difference-between-express-and-implied-consent/.

"What's the Most Commonly Used Phlebotomy Equipment? From Scrubs to..." n.d. PhlebotomyU. Accessed June 10, 2022. https://phlebotomyu.com/phlebotomy-equipment/.

"What's the Most Commonly Used Phlebotomy Equipment? From Scrubs to..." n.d. PhlebotomyU. Accessed June 16, 2022. https://phlebotomyu.com/phlebotomy-equipment/.

"What to Do if the Patient Feels Faint." n.d. Laboratory Continuing Education. Accessed June 16, 2022. https://www.labce.com/spg549504_what_to_do_if_the_patient_feels_.

"Which Blood Tests Require Fasting Beforehand?" n.d. PhlebotomyU. Accessed June 10, 2022. https://phlebotomyu.com/which-blood-tests-require-fasting/.

"Which Blood Tests Require Fasting Beforehand?" n.d. PhlebotomyU. Accessed June 16, 2022. https://phlebotomyu.com/which-blood-tests-require-fasting/.

Wolters Kluwer Health. n.d. Chapter 13: Nonblood Specimens and Tests Chapter 13: Nonblood Specimens and Tests Objectives Objectives (cont'd) Objectives (c. Accessed June 16, 2022. https://www.ccctc.k12.oh.us/Downloads/Chapter_13.pdf.

World Health Organization. 2009. WHO Guidelines on Hand Hygiene in Health Care: First Global Patient Safety Challenge : Clean Care is Safer Care. N.p.: World Health Organization, Patient Safety.

World Health Organization. 2010. "Best practices in phlebotomy - WHO Guidelines on Drawing Blood." NCBI. https://www.ncbi.nlm.nih.gov/books/NBK138665/.

World Health Organization. 2010. "Explaining the procedure to a patient - WHO Guidelines on Drawing Blood." NCBI. https://www.ncbi.nlm.nih.gov/books/NBK138658/.

World Health Organization. 2010. "Implementing best phlebotomy practices

- WHO Guidelines on Drawing Blood." NCBI. https://www.ncbi.nlm.nih. gov/books/NBK138655/.

Zaoutis, Lisa B., and Vincent W. Chiang. n.d. "Comprehensive Pediatric Hospital Medicine." Accessed June 16, 2022. https://books.google.co.ma/books?id=7E-jugzT7wNQC&pg=PA1262&redir_esc=y#v=onepage&q&f=false.